*The translation of this book
into English was made possible through
a grant from the Adolf Amram Fund*

*Rebirth*

# REBIRTH

*\* The story of
Eliezer Ben-Yehudah
and the
modern Hebrew language by*

## D V O R A H   O M E R

*Translated from the
Hebrew by Ruth Rasnic*

*The Jewish Publication Society
of America
Philadelphia   5732–1972*

*Pictures on page 99 (bottom) and page 187 (bottom)*
*are courtesy of Zionist Archives and Library, New*
*York; all others generously loaned by Dola*
*Ben-Yehudah Wittman.*

*Rebirth

# * *one*

"Eliezer! Eliezer! The child, Eliezer . . . hurry, please hurry!" said the pale and frightened Dvorah as she burst into the study.

Eliezer tore his eyes away from his books and notes and looked at her in surprise. "What is it, Dvorah? What's happened?"

"Eliezer . . ." Dvorah was shivering. "The child . . . there'll be an accident. . . . You must do something. Oh, Eliezer!"

The father realized that he could get nothing out of his wife, so he hurried to the adjoining room. He was about to open the door when Dvorah's frightened voice stopped him. "No. Don't, Eliezer! We mustn't frighten him. This must be done quietly or else there can be a terrible accident. Oh, Eliezer, I am so frightened!" she said, wringing her hands.

The surprised man bent down and peeked through the keyhole. He beheld a shocking scene. His three-year-old son, Ben-Zion, was sitting on the floor playing with a black, glittering snake. The snake was wound around the boy's bare feet and was raising itself up to the level of his face. The child was picking the snake up by its tail and gleefully throwing it down again.

"What can we do, Eliezer? Something must be

done. The snake will bite him. Oh, Eliezer, do something!" wept the mother.

"They seem to be good friends," said Eliezer, unable to trust his own eyes. "We mustn't go in. We might frighten the snake, and then it's sure to hurt the child."

So the parents stood behind the door, bending down in turn and peeking through the keyhole at the weird scene.

The two went on playing in this manner for a long time—the happy, delighted boy and the snake, winding itself, uncoiling itself, and letting the boy do as he wished with its body.

Suddenly the snake slithered away, slid along the floor, and vanished into a crack in the gray stone wall. This was just what the mother had been waiting for. She dashed into the room, grabbed her son, and hugged him to her bosom.

"Ben-Zion, my child," she whispered. "My darling child, my love. You have given Imma such a fright."

"Amimal, amimal," murmured the boy, who did not know how to name his new playmate.

"Say snake, Ben-Zion. This is a snake," said the father, approaching his son. "Snake, Ben-Zion. Little black snake. Pretty snake. Go on, child. Say it."

"Knase, knase," repeated the child happily. "Knase, knase. Oh, aaa knase." The three-year-old child was unable to speak. All he could do was stutter a few broken words and syllables.

"Pretty black snake. Go on, child. Repeat it after me," the father tried again.

"He doesn't know how to speak," Dvorah muttered. "Our son can't speak. You should hear the way the neighbors' children talk. Bechar's youngest child is five months younger than our Ben-Zion, and he speaks fluently. The daughter of—"

"I don't want to hear any more!" Eliezer interrupted her and went back to his room.

"Knase, knase!" The child ran after his father. He felt he had somehow disappointed him and wanted to please him.

"Abba, knase amimal. Aaa amimal, dah, knase," he stuttered, trying pitifully to form a proper sentence. But Eliezer was already deep in his work and paid no attention to the child.

"Come here, Ben-Zion darling. Don't disturb Abba in his work," said Dvorah, as she took the child by his hand. "Come, my pet. I'll put you to bed."

"Imma, Imma, amimal knase!" The small boy was excited and delighted. He was thrilled to have discovered a new friend in the form of a black snake.

Little Ben-Zion was very lonely. He had no playmates. His father refused to let him go outside to the cobbled yard and play with the neighbors' children. He was always kept indoors. Children never came to play with him, and he never went to play with them. He had only two friends: Zimri the cat, and the dog, whom Ben-Zion called "Goggie." It was an ugly little dog, yellowish white, the color of the pale and sickly Ben-Zion, who already suffered from recurring bouts of malaria. But Ben-Zion loved the miserable cur with all his heart. He would spend the entire day with his two playmates, the dog and the cat. Now that he had discovered an additional playmate he was happy and excited.

The mother put the child to bed. She was filled with pity at the sight of his thin body. She caressed his pale little face, kissed his head, and very softly, as though singing to herself, began humming an old nursery song which her mother used to sing to her in a now distant childhood.

*"Na sinyem volno okeania* (upon a blue ocean)," sang the mother, and the child stared up at her with his lovely large eyes, listening to the strange, unfamiliar sound and the soft, melodic tune. *"Na sinyem volno okeania,"* sang Dvorah, the tears flowing down from her eyes. She was weeping for her own terrible loneliness. Suddenly she was overwhelmed by a wave of longing for her far-off family. She wept for her pale little son, who was so different from other children, for the evil prophecies made by friends and neighbors cautioning her that unless she and the boy's father acted differently, the child would become hopelessly dumb. She was sorry for the young child lying so pale and sad in his bed. What would be his fate? Were they really doing a grave injustice and actually ruining his tender soul? Why didn't he speak like all other children his age? Dvorah was so immersed in her sad thoughts that she did not hear the door open.

"Dvorah!" thundered Eliezer. "What are you doing?"

She had never seen him so furious before. His face had turned a frightening blue-black. In anger, he tore the paper which he held in his hand into tiny shreds and threw them on the floor.

"You are singing this song to him? This song which I have forbidden! How dare you? You have done this to my son? You have spoiled everything which I built up. You have corrupted the child's soul!"

He went over to her, shaking with fury. Then he began coughing and choking. A reddish foam collected on his lips. He clutched at his chest and seemed about to collapse with pain. "Eliezer, my husband." Dvorah ran over to him.

"Go away from me!" he said, thrusting her aside so roughly that she almost fell down. She sat on the single chair which stood in the corner of the room and hid her face in her hands; her shoulders shook.

The child felt that something terrible had taken place in his room. He got out of bed, terrified, and ran over to his mother. He hugged her shoulders, stroked her bent head, and when he saw the tears falling between her fingers, turned to his father and said in an imperative tone, "Abba! Don't you shout at Imma! You mustn't, Abba!"

"Dvorah! Did you hear him, Dvorah?" Eliezer ran over to his son and picked him up. "He spoke! Ben-Zion has just uttered his first sentence. Did you hear him, Dvorah?"

"He spoke, Ben-Zion spoke." The mother embraced her son and her tears of frustrated anger turned into tears of joy. "He won't be dumb! He'll be like all other children. He'll talk like everyone else. Oh, my child, my child!"

"He'll talk better than everyone else. You just wait and see!" Eliezer said in a tone of authority.

The delighted and excited parents put the child back in his bed and left the room.

Eliezer went back to his study, intending to continue working. He had so much work ahead of him, and he had to finish it. The child who had spoken his first whole sentence that evening, had proved that he —Ben-Yehudah—was right. People regarded him as an unnatural father, a man who treated his only son with cruelty, a heartless man, an infidel. Some even thought he was mad. But he knew that it could be done. Now he had to prove to everybody that he could do the thing that seemed impossible. The quotation which he had hung over his desk—TIME IS SHORT AND THERE IS MUCH WORK TO BE DONE!—seemed to beckon him. He bent over his books and began writing with renewed energy.

Dvorah sat by the window, staring at the distant mountain range along the horizon, which was slowly being covered by the blanket of night. She could see the gray, winding lanes of Jerusalem and the large stones of the city wall. Her thoughts carried her far away, across the sea, to the past, to the days of her youth in the small town in Russia in the second half of the nineteenth century. . . .

## * two

"Come here, Dvorah, come and see whom I have brought with me," said the father, smiling, as he opened the front door. The sturdy girl with the black braids walked over to her father and looked at the person at his side. She saw a young lad who seemed about her own age. He was wearing a long black coat, and long, fair earlocks curled down from under his hat.

"Do you like him, my child? This is Eliezer," the father said, smiling at his embarrassed daughter. And as a matter of fact, she did like him. Her heart beat faster. She knew why she was excited at the sight of the boy. She had often read about this emotion in her father's large books. She was now feeling the first flutter of love.

"What's the matter, Dvorah?" her father asked the blushing girl, who had lowered her eyes. "Where are your manners? Or perhaps you've swallowed your tongue, God forbid!" He turned to the other children who were surrounding him and the youth and were chattering happily. "I have brought you a new brother. I have six children, and he will make the seventh. I found him asleep in the synagogue, hungry and nearly frozen. He left home because he wants to study. Are you ready to accept him as a member of our family?"

"Yes, yes!" they all shouted.

"Only our eldest daughter has remained silent," said the father, turning to Dvorah once more.

"Oh yes, I agree!" replied Dvorah, raising her eyes to the lad again. She blushed as her eyes met his bold gaze. "Would you like me to be your teacher and teach you foreign languages?" she asked quietly, while her heart beat wildly.

"With the greatest of pleasure," Eliezer replied.

"Come with me," she whispered. "There is something I would like to show you."

Eliezer followed Dvorah shyly. She led him to the

library and pointed to the book-laden shelves. "I will teach you to read all these books," she assured him. "They contain such beautiful stories."

Eliezer stared at the large library. The books were bound in thick, dark leather and were embossed with golden letters. "Can I read one of them right away?" he asked.

"Of course you can. Only you must learn French first. Here, have a look. This is a fascinating story of a man who lived alone on an island for many years —Robinson Crusoe," she said, as she took the thick volume down from the shelf.

"I know this book. I began reading it. But in Hebrew it was such a small book, and my uncle wouldn't let me read it. He said that it was sacrilege to publish books in the language of the Holy Scriptures. He beat me and ordered me to stop reading such books. I would love to find out how the book ended."

"Nobody will beat you here," Dvorah promised. "Come, I'll tell you how the story ended, and then I'll teach you to read. Someday you will be able to read all these books in French, German, and Russian."

Dvorah opened the book. "Come and sit here next to me," she said. They sat down on the sofa, looked at the color prints, and Dvorah told him the story of Robinson Crusoe. From time to time, as she turned a leaf over, her finger touched Eliezer's fingers, and she was filled with a thrilling sensation.

Her mother abruptly opened the library door. "Dvorah," she said, "our guest is frozen stiff and starving. You had better put off your lesson till tomorrow. Come along, my boy. I'll give you something to eat and a change of clothes."

*Dvorah Ben-Yehudah, first wife of Eliezer Ben-Yehudah, mother of Ben-Zion Yehudah (Itamar Ben-Avi)*

Next morning Dvorah was faced by a handsome, clean, and neatly combed boy. It was impossible to recognize last night's miserable visitor. He appeared much taller in his new clothes, young and more energetic. He had even given up his earlocks and his long, dark clothes to win his teacher's appreciation.

Every day Dvorah and Eliezer would sit side by side in the library. Dvorah taught and explained, and Eliezer took in every word avidly.

The boy was very talented. He learned the languages which Dvorah taught him with remarkable speed. He read a great deal. His fingers would rustle through the books feverishly. His appetite for learning seemed endless.

Dvorah's love for Eliezer grew from day to day. She could feel that he loved her, too. He would look at her admiringly—but he never said a word. Dvorah wanted him to speak of his love. But the bashful youth kept his love locked deep in his heart, indicating it only by the expression in his eyes.

Eliezer became a member of the Yonas family. Shlomo Yonas, the father, was a wealthy Jew, the owner of a brewery. He was very generous toward his adopted son, whom he treated like his own children. Eliezer had a warm home, nice clothes, good food, and was receiving an excellent education; and above all, he had the love of a mother and a father.

Two years went by. During this time Dvorah taught him all she knew. Then her father decided to send the talented boy to school, in order to widen his horizons and increase his knowledge.

Parting was difficult.

"You'll forget me," whispered Dvorah with tears in her eyes.

"I won't forget you. I owe you so much for all you've done for me."

"Isn't there anything else you would like to tell me?" Dvorah asked.

The boy blushed.

"I love you, Eliezer. From the minute I first saw you. And what about you?" murmured Dvorah, lowering her eyes and waiting for his answer with a palpitating heart.

"Me too . . . ," the boy began, and went no further. The mother had just entered the room.

"It's time to say good-bye," said the good-hearted woman. "I have prepared your bags and some food for your journey. And you mustn't forget to put your warm overcoat on. I don't like this cough of yours. And look after yourself when you are far away from home. And another thing. If your cough gets any worse, you must see a doctor about it," the woman continued, plying him with good advice.

The young couple were not left alone again. The brothers and sisters gathered around Eliezer, and the entire family went to the railway station to see him off and wish him good luck.

Years went by. Eliezer traveled far and wide, studying all the time. He wrote many letters to his adoptive family during his travels, telling them about his life and studies. He also wrote to Dvorah. In his long letters he told her about his belief that the place for the Jews was Palestine, and that he intended to dedicate his life to reviving the Hebrew language. It must no longer be a holy tongue, he wrote, used only for prayers. It must become a modern, living language—the language of the Jewish people. It should be used constantly, in place of the many languages that the Jews presently employed. He wrote in a flowery style, describing his plans for the revival of the Hebrew language.

Dvorah would swallow the words, searching for a message of love. But she never found it in his letters. Had he forgotten her? Or was there someone else he preferred? These thoughts gave her no rest. She rejected all the suitors who came to court her. She had made up her mind: if she could not have Eliezer, she would never marry.

Years passed, and finally the great day arrived. Eliezer came home. He looked pale and sickly. He was surrounded by the whole family. They all hugged and kissed him warmly, except for Dvorah, who stood aside shyly. That evening they had no time to themselves. Dvorah kept looking at him and wondering what he was feeling. When the children finally went to bed, Eliezer whispered to Dvorah, "There is something I want to discuss with you privately. Can you come out for a walk in the garden with me?"

She followed to the garden with trembling legs.

"You're so pretty," said Eliezer, looking at her closely. "All these years I've been thinking about you. But I had forgotten just how lovely you are."

"Oh Eliezer," she said. "I have also been thinking about you all these years, and all the time my heart was truly yours."

Eliezer's face darkened. In the moonlight she

could see a set face and a mouth clamped in determination.

"What I have to tell you this evening, Dvorah, is that you must tear me out of your heart. We will never be able to marry."

"But why not?" she asked, her eyes filling with tears. "Do you love somebody else?"

"No," he whispered. "It's you I love."

"In that case, what's wrong?" Dvorah couldn't understand.

"I am very sick. The doctors have diagnosed tuberculosis, and I was told that I have only a few years to live. I intend to devote these last years of my life to my people. I am going to Jerusalem. There, I will do everything in my power to restore the Hebrew language to the Jewish people."

"I shall go with you, Eliezer. I shall be at your side, look after you, care for you. I shall help you with your work."

"Dvorah, you are so gentle and sweet. But you're used to such an easy life in your father's home. Life in Palestine is very hard."

"I'll come with you if you love me and want me to!" she declared.

"I do love you. But—"

"Let's go inside and tell my parents."

The parents were amazed to see their daughter dragging the embarrassed Eliezer into the house. Never before had their daughter looked so lovely and radiant.

"Mother! Father! We are going to get married. We are going to Jerusalem. Oh, Mother! I am so happy!"

The parents could do nothing to deter their

daughter. They gave their consent to the marriage with misgivings. After a brief period they said good-bye to the young couple with tears in their eyes and worry in their hearts.

The journey to Palestine took Eliezer and Dvorah a long time. Finally, they reached the port of Jaffa after a long and tiresome trip. From there, they made their way to Jerusalem.

This was not the Jerusalem which Dvorah had visualized from the Bible: the glorious city of David, bustling with life and color, the city of the prophets, the city for which the Jews of the world had so fervently yearned. The Jerusalem they came to was a smelly, dirty Middle Eastern town of winding alleys and miserable sheds, dilapidated huts and broken down shops. The vendors—mostly Arabs—screamed praises of their wares at the tops of their voices. Everything seemed strange and poor.

After a prolonged search, Dvorah and Eliezer finally managed to find a miserable little apartment near the wall of the Old City. With great difficulty, Eliezer found a job as a reporter on a Hebrew paper which was published in Jerusalem. Dvorah began doing all kinds of housework, which she had never done before. Life was hard, but she was ready for everything as long as she stayed at the side of her adored husband. For his sake she gave up her mother tongue, Russian, and began speaking Hebrew. She would string one word to another, making small sentences. Slowly and patiently she learned the new language. In time, Hebrew was the only language spoken in the Ben-Yehudah home.

When Dvorah was due to give birth to their first child, Eliezer demanded that the baby must hear only Hebrew. She agreed to this and promised to keep it secluded and apart from other children. She even agreed to keep it locked up at home until the child was seven years old—"so that it shall hear no other language, and so that its ears will not be polluted by the sound of foreign languages," Eliezer explained.

The child was a son, whom they named Ben-Zion. Dvorah kept her word. The child was locked in the apartment, and people who spoke no Hebrew were not allowed near him. Everybody felt sorry for the poor child and spoke of the parents' cruelty. The boy seemed to be retarded, for though he could understand everything that was said to him, he could not speak.

Now, finally, he had uttered his first sentence. Was he really beginning to speak? Would he be like all other children? Or was Eliezer mistaken? Was Hebrew, in fact, only the language of the Bible and prayers, and not to be revived and turned into a modern language? If her husband was mistaken, it would be her child—her beloved Ben-Zion—who would pay the price.

Dvorah rose slowly and heavily from her seat. She was tired, her head ached, and she was hungry. Her husband and her son had eaten the loaf which she had baked that morning, and she had not eaten a thing. There was no more money for food. What were they going to eat tomorrow? What about the landlord, who had threatened to throw them out unless they paid their rent? Feeling depressed, she lay on her bed and watched Eliezer, who was standing near the tall desk in the corner of the room. A small oil lamp lit up his corner and threw flickering shadows on the walls, the piles of books and papers, and his hard, stubborn face. Her husband was immersed in his work and seemed like a man engaged in religious worship. He would succeed. "He must succeed!" she murmured to herself, and fell asleep with a feeling of relief.

## * *three*

Dvorah was up with the first rays of the sun. She opened her eyes and saw Eliezer at his desk in the corner. She was not at all surprised to see him up so early. She was quite used to seeing him poring over his books and papers at night and then, after a few hours' sleep, carrying on with his work until it was time for him to go to the newspaper office. This time, however, a completely different scene met her eyes. Eliezer was surrounded by colored picture books, and Ben-Zion's toys were spread all around him on the floor.

"What are you doing, Eliezer?" she asked in amazement, as she went over to him.

"Good morning, my dear," he replied, as he raised his eyes from the books. "Come here a second. Look at this! Remember the way Ben-Zion began speaking yesterday? The next step will be the question stage. He will ask us questions about anything and everything that surrounds him: toys, flowers, birds, insects —everything. And we must have a suitable answer for all his questions. This is what I've been doing the last few hours.

"Here, have a look," he said, pointing to a picture of a flower. "This is a *vered*. Try and remember. *Vered*. And this insect, the yellow one that flutters so prettily, I'll call a *parpar*. I am looking for words and names out of the ancient sources, or at least looking for a suitable root and trying to adjust it. If I can't find anything suitable, I look for something in the Aramaic or Arabic, which are closely related Semitic languages, and when there is nothing I can find there, I simply make up a word. I prefer a word in broken Hebrew to the most wonderful usage in a foreign tongue."

"What are you going to call this charming couple," asked Dvorah as she picked up a pair of stuffed animals from the floor. They were a present from the grandparents in Russia and had arrived only a few days earlier.

"These, of course, are male and female bears, a *dov* and a *dubah*. Don't you remember them from the Bible?"

"That's right," replied Dvorah, "so they are. But surely there is no name for this in the Bible," she said pointing to the picture of a doll with a round, chubby face, curly hair, a small pouting red mouth, and a dress made of lace. "What are you going to call this?"

"You are quite right. What am I going to call it? Just a moment, let me think. . . . I have it. *Buba*—doll. How do you like it?"

"*Buba,*" said Dvorah, as she repeated the word after him. "It has a nice sound. Children will have no difficulty pronouncing it. I like the word *buba.*"

"I must return to my work, Dvorah. There are so many new words to discover. I don't want my son's vocabulary to be lacking a single word. Eventually I am going to write a few songs for him, and you can set them to music. You must sing our son many songs. All in Hebrew, of course."

Dvorah walked over to the sleeping child. "My darling," she murmured, "your mother is going to do everything in the world for you. I will give you everything under the sun, so that you will never feel lonely and will become like all other children. I will give you everything, everything on earth."

Then she remembered that there was no food in the house. She went over to Eliezer somewhat hesitantly. "I am sorry to have to interfere once more," she murmured, "but there is no food in the house."

"Don't worry, Dvorah," Eliezer told her. "I will go over to the pawnbroker and pawn my gold watch. I will get enough money to enable us to buy flour, oil, olives . . ."

"Your gold watch," whispered Dvorah. "But that is the watch I gave you on our wedding day."

"Don't worry, Dvorah," he tried to cheer her up. "I forgot to mention that I have another job, in addition to my work on the newspaper. Starting next week, I am going to work as a Hebrew master in the new Alliance school. I will earn plenty of money. We shall be able to redeem the watch in no time."

That day, after baking two loaves of bread, Dvorah began converting the upper courtyard, next to the railing of their window, into a kindergarten for Ben-Zion. She washed the gray stones with sand and water until they were white and bright. She collected a few empty cans and old cases, filled them with loose soil, and planted a few flower seeds and various vegetables. On the walls of the inner yard she hung bright pictures of birds and flowers, cut out of the books which she had brought with her from Russia.

"Look, Ben-Zion. This is a *parpar!*" She uttered the new word with reverence.

*"Parpar, parpar,"* the child repeated.

"Pretty *parpar,* yellow *parpar.* Come on, darling, repeat Imma's words."

"Pity *parpar,* lellow *parpar,*" said the child, wrinkling his forehead with the strain.

"Oh darling, this is lovely!" she said, hugging him warmly. The miracle had indeed taken place. The child, who until yesterday could utter only a few broken words, suddenly began repeating every word which came out of her mouth. He seemed to have cast off the stammering hesitation which had hindered his development. "This, Ben-Zion, is a *buba!*" she said as she placed her latest creation before him—a figure made of rags, with a face outlined in colored cotton.

*"Buba,"* he cried as he grabbed hold of the doll. "Pretty *buba!*"

The news that Eliezer's son had started to speak spread all through Jerusalem. Saturday evening, after kiddush, people began to gather at the home of the Ben-Yehudahs. Eliezer stood in the doorway, greeting the guests. Everyone who wanted to enter had to prove to Eliezer that he could speak Hebrew. People who spoke no Hebrew were made to promise that they would be silent in the boy's presence.

"Now that my son has actually begun speaking, he must not hear a single sound in a foreign language," he warned his guests.

There were many people in the Ben-Yehudah house that evening, including rabbis, representatives of the community, and young pioneers who came from distant villages. Elderly neighbors held Ben-Zion in their arms. They hugged and kissed him, and were thrilled when the child repeated everything that was said to him. Pregnant women went over to him and touched him, in hopes that their offspring would be like this clever child who spoke the holy tongue.

"Long may Eliezer, the miracle-maker, live," cried the guests as they raised their glasses.

"And Dvorah, his virtuous spouse," they added, beaming at the excited woman.

"To the health of the first Hebrew child," cried the young pioneers, lifting Ben-Zion and passing him from hand to hand and from shoulder to shoulder. Ben-Zion had never seen so many people before.

There were some who did not partake in the merrymaking. One angry-looking, long-bearded rabbi stood apart. He stood looking at the child furiously, saying nothing at all. When Dvorah walked over to Ben-Zion and whispered in his ear that he should leave the room and go to the toilet, the rabbi could no longer contain his anger.

"Sacrilege! This is sacrilege!" he said, shaking with fury. "You have turned the holy tongue, the tongue of prayers and the Torah, into the language of the streets, in which one can talk of toilets." He stomped out of the house, banging the door shut.

The rabbi's anger confused the guests. They began to leave the house one by one, departing in embarrassment. The last to leave was a good friend of the family, Reb Yechiel Michal Piness. Piness had kept still all evening and had seemed lost in deep musing and sadness.

When Dvorah finally put Ben-Zion to bed, Piness began speaking. "Dvorah and Eliezer, my friends. I rejoice together with you at your son's development. But..." he hesitated for a moment and went on. "This is your first child. I have raised my own children and have seen many others. Ben-Zion has begun to speak. He repeats everything you say, parrot fashion. Still, there is nothing spectacular or exciting about this— even a trained animal can pick up tricks after years of training. The child has learned only a smattering of words and sentences. I am really sorry to have to tell you this, but he is still very backward for his age. A child his age, a child of three-and-a-half, is a young *person*. He can sing, speak fluently, tell stories. Your son is still unable to do all these. His few mutterings in Hebrew are no great achievement.

"My good friend," he said, turning around to Eliezer and gripping both his hands, "I support your battle for the revival of Hebrew. But leave this for us adults. Let the child alone. It is impossible to bring up a child in a language which has been dormant for two thousand years. He must be raised in a living language, a juicy language which contains a word for everything. Speak to him in French, German, Russian, or Yiddish. Any language will do. Sing to him, tell him stories, enrich his soul. It is still not too late, my friend. Save your son's soul. Save him from the dulling of his senses, from backwardness, dumbness."

"I will never speak anything but Hebrew to my son!" declared Eliezer.

"But Eliezer, you are sacrificing your own son," Piness remonstrated. "This time the Angel of God will not come down to save him from a terrible fate." Tears had welled in Piness's eyes. "Have pity on the child! You are never going to succeed in your venture!"

"If I do not succeed with this child, I shall try with my second, third, and fourth child, until I do!" Eliezer gazed into his friend's eyes with stubbornness and determination.

Dvorah bent over her sleeping child, cuddling him in her arms. She was trembling.

## * four

Months went by. Little Ben-Zion, who was now four years old, picked up words with amazing speed. Everything which he had absorbed in his long period of dumbness and stammering burst out like a tidal wave. He spoke, sang, told stories, asked questions, gave answers. His parents were overjoyed. Eliezer spent all his spare time searching for new words for his son's world. He did not want a single word to be missing from the boy's loud and chatty vocabulary.

Occasionally Ben-Zion himself made up new words. Whenever he wanted to express something and was unable to think of the right word, he would immediately make one up—to his father's joy and his mother's delight. A friend bought him a shiny toy that spun on the floor, and Ben-Zion called out in glee to his mother: "Have a look, Imma. See how the *sevivon* turns. I have a pretty little *sevivon.*"

"What a nice word that is, a *sevivon,*" said Dvorah excitedly, as she kissed her son's head. Little Ben-Zion felt very proud at teaching his father a new word for a change. The noisy toy which he received for Purim he named a *ra'ashan,* because it rattled so. When his mother bathed him in the tub in the kitchen and soaped his head, he begged, "Imma, *al tisabni oti.*"

"Dvorah, what is this word I just heard?" asked Eliezer from the next room.

"Ben-Zion has asked me not to soap him," smiled Dvorah.

"*Lesabain,* to soap, a verb from the word *sabon,* soap. That's very good," said Eliezer and immediately noted the word down in his notebook.

The handsome and intelligent child captivated everyone who visited them. People would hold discussions with him, as they would with an adult, and enjoy the spontaneous new words with which he studded his Hebrew. Even Piness, who for a long time had been worried about the child and angry at what was being done to him, had to admit Eliezer's success.

"You have won your point, Ben-Yehudah, you certainly have," he said after a long conversation with the four-year-old Ben-Zion. "This child is a prodigy. Please don't be angry at me for being so sharp with you. I did it because I was deeply concerned over the child's welfare."

The parents were proud and happy. Suddenly the world seemed to smile upon them. About the same time, Ben-Yehudah started his own newspaper. Through it, he hoped to express his opinions and spread the Hebrew language. He thought that he would have many subscribers and that their financial situation would improve. Everything appeared full of promise.

Little Ben-Zion was often very lonely. The courtyard which his mother named "the kindergarten" shut him off from the world, and Ben-Zion used to pace in it like a prisoner in his cell. The large iron door facing the street was always locked, and Ben-Zion was only allowed to look down at the street but not to go down to play. He used to sit by the railing and watch the children playing below. He was not allowed to go down and make friends with them. He used to sit there for many hours and gaze at them with longing. By that time his friends, the animals, had vanished. Zimri the cat just left one morning and never came back. The father had ordered the puppy's removal, too. Ben-Yehudah could not stand having animals in the house.

"Imma, please let me go down. Let me go out for a minute, please!" he would beg his mother with tears in his eyes.

But the mother was obliged to keep her word to her husband not to permit Ben-Zion to play with children who knew no Hebrew until he was seven years old. She did not let him out.

"Imma, why am I always alone? Why don't I have any friends?" the boy would persist.

"Ben-Zion, darling," she would say, "I am here with you. I am here all the time. Come, let's play with your ball. Or perhaps you would like to hear a story? You are never alone, sweetheart. Imma is always here with you."

"You are a good Imma," the little boy said as he hugged Dvorah. "Only, I want a friend—a boy."

"You will soon have a friend." Dvorah whispered her secret in her son's ear. "Very soon—in a month's time—you will have a tiny brother or sister. You will no longer be alone. You will always have someone to be with you. You will be able to play and be happy."

A brother, a young brother. Ben-Zion waited anxiously for the birth of his brother—for in his heart he hoped it would be a boy, not a girl. Girls were so talkative and irritating. If he had a brother they could always play ball together, run around the courtyard, invent games, and play with all his toys—just like the children playing in the street.

But when the brother, who was named Avichayil, was born, Ben-Zion was in for a shock. It was impossible to play with this tiny, crying creature who had such a creased, red face. And now that the baby was born, his mother was busy with him and no longer had any time for Ben-Zion. He discovered that he was lonelier than ever.

One day he sat in the courtyard watching the

children play in the street below. It was a lively and interesting game, and he decided he must join them. The front door was always locked. Still, his mother was very busy with Avichayil and would not miss him. He climbed on the iron railing and slowly slid down to the street. It was a difficult thing to do. The rough edges of the wall scratched his hands and legs, and when he jumped down he hit his head on the pavement. He disregarded the pain. He ran to the children, excited at reaching them at long last.

"Can I join you?" he called happily.

The children watched the small boy approach them. His earlocks had been cut short, he was dressed like a young cossack, and on his head he wore a red tarbush. What was even stranger was that the unknown boy addressed them in a foreign tongue. They were afraid of him.

"I'd like to play with you," he repeated. The boys were afraid and began to run away, shouting to each other in Yiddish, a language which Ben-Zion could not understand. He could only make out his father's name and the word "crazy," which is the same in Yiddish as in Hebrew.

He could hear voices shouting from the distance: "Crazy! crazy!" The words stabbed his heart like a knife.

"Why do they call me crazy? Why won't they play with me? What have I done to them?"

He sat and cried on the street corner. The blow on his head and the cuts and scratches were painful. But the thing that hurt him most was the terrible loneliness and the children's jeers. Tears flowed down his cheeks. Suddenly he heard a weak whimper. He looked up and saw a small dog next to him, wagging its tail. The dog seemed miserable and lonely. He felt very sorry for the poor little animal. He picked it up and began talking to it in Hebrew. The dog seemed to understand. It looked up at him with affection and warmth and started licking his tearful face with its tongue.

"Poor little dog. My poor little pet. You will be my friend, won't you? You will never laugh at me or call me crazy. You and I will always be friends, won't we?"

The dog barked in agreement and licked his hand happily.

For a long time Ben-Zion sat on the corner, his new friend in his arms. Finally he fell asleep.

Ben-Zion woke up to the sound of frantic voices calling him. He looked around, frightened. Everything was dark.

"Ben-Zion, where are you, Ben-Zion?" He could make out his parents' voices. They could not be far off.

He sat without moving, hugging the dog to his heart. "They mustn't find me," he told himself. "They will take the dog away from me. I am going to hide and they are never going to find me. I am not going back home. That's settled."

It took a long time for Eliezer and Dvorah to discover their young son's hiding place.

"Where were you?" Eliezer demanded angrily.

"Why did you go down?" his mother asked excitedly.

"I wanted to play with the children. But they don't like me. They ran away from me and called me crazy.

But now I have a real friend. He loves me. Oh Abba, please don't take him away from me," he begged.

"All right, you can keep the dog," said the father. It suddenly occurred to him just how miserable and lonely his son actually was. "But remember, you may address him only in Hebrew. Who knows," he added as he smiled at Dvorah, "when people see that even a dog can understand Hebrew, they may begin to believe that the language has a future."

"I promise! I promise! I will speak only Hebrew to the dog. I am going to teach him Hebrew," Ben-Zion agreed readily. After all, he could speak no other language.

"What are we going to call him?" he asked on the way home.

"Let's name him Speedy," Eliezer suggested.

Ben-Zion held the dog in his arms as he took him home. He was very happy. From now on he would have a true and loyal friend, with whom he could play, to whom he could talk. He would never be lonely again.

## * five

Speedy was indeed a good and loyal friend. He was a glossy gray-black hound, and he was strong and healthy. To Ben-Zion he proved to be more than a friend; he was also a brave and loyal guardian whenever the boy succeeded in getting away to the street. Speedy would walk at his side, baring the frightening jaws of a six-month-old puppy, and bark at everybody who tried to approach the child.

Ben-Zion no longer needed the boys who played in the alleys and the courtyards. Speedy loved him with all the warmth and devotion of an affectionate dog. He understood his commands and carried them out.

"Come here," Ben-Zion would order, and the dog would hurry over to him. "Sit down!" The dog would sit. "Down, down!" The dog would lie on the floor. "Bark!" Ben-Zion would order, and to the boy's great delight, Speedy would bark loudly.

Young Avichayil, who had just begun crawling on the floor, began to join them. He would pull the dog's tail, place his fingers in Speedy's mouth, and laugh with the delighted gurgle of a baby. "Peedy, Peedy," he would call to him in baby talk. The dog would lie down on the floor beside him and lick his face, and Ben-Zion would stand viewing the scene happily—his two friends playing together so nicely. There was one thing to mar his happiness: here he was with such a clever and talented dog, and there was nobody to show him off to.

His father hated dogs. Like many other Jews at the time, Eliezer was afraid of dogs. True, he overcame his intense dislike and agreed to let the dog stay in the house for his son's sake. But Ben-Zion realized that if he was to keep his loyal friend, Speedy must be kept away from his father. Nor could he boast about the dog to his mother, as he would have liked to do, for she was now carrying her third child and was always busy and tired. What could he do? He was eager to show off his clever dog, who understood Hebrew and carried out all his orders.

One day he slid down to the street. It was noon of a pleasant autumn day. A slight breeze was blowing, and light clouds were floating in the air. Ben-Zion inhaled the fresh sweet air.

"Isn't it lovely here?" he asked his dog. "What a shame we can't go out more often. I like being outside, don't you?"

The dog replied with a gay bark. The two friends jumped up and down, leaped over sewage streams which flowed down the alley, and ran happily along the street. After a while Ben-Zion noticed a group of children on a street corner. These were children from Meah Shearim, the most religious and fanatic quarter of Jerusalem. They wore long coats and had long earlocks. Ben-Zion went up to them and began showing off with his dog.

"Come!" he ordered, and the dog trotted over, wagging his tail. "Sit down, Speedy!" The dog immediately squatted at his feet and licked his shoes.

Ben-Zion looked around, hoping to see admiring and envious looks on the children's faces. How could anybody not be impressed by such tricks?

The children huddled together in the corner, and whispered.

"Bark, Speedy!" Ben-Zion went on with his show. The dog began barking loudly.

When the children heard the barking, they jumped back.

"Quiet, Speedy! Quiet!" Ben-Zion calmed his dog. He did not want the boys to run off. On the contrary, he wanted them to come closer. Now he was sure they were going to ask him to be friends with them and ask to play with his dog.

Ben-Zion smiled at them happily and said, "Come here! Don't be afraid of Speedy, he's a good dog. He won't harm you at all. You can stroke him if you wish. It's quite all right. I—" Suddenly he stopped. What on earth was going on?

A volley of small stones suddenly struck the boy and his dog. The children surrounded them, bent to the ground, picked up more stones, and threw them at the boy, screaming with rage. Once more he heard the terrible words: "Crazy, infidel, holy tongue!" and many other words which he had never heard before. For a second he was shocked. Then he turned around, broke through the circle of boys, and ran home as fast as his feet could carry him.

His mother was not home. He walked quietly into the kitchen. His father was busy with his work and had not even noticed that he had left the house without permission. The boy's lips were dry and his face seemed to be on fire. He filled a tin cup from the great water jug and drank the cool liquid. "Is that you, Ben-Zion?" he heard his father's voice say from the next room. The door opened, and his father stood on the threshold, looking surprised and worried at his wild-eyed, panting, and bleeding son.

"What's wrong, Ben-Zion?" he asked.

"They stoned us. I was out there with Speedy.

They—" Then he remembered. How could he have run away and left his dog?

"Ben-Zion, where are you going?" cried Eliezer.

Ben-Zion did not reply. He dashed outside and hurried back to the corner. The alley was deserted. There was no one around.

There was a small pile of stones in the middle of the road.

"Speedy, Speedy!" he shouted. "Where are you, Speedy?"

Silence.

His heart sensed that something terrible had happened. He started removing the stones with trembling fingers. There, under the pile of stones, lay his Speedy, in a pool of blood.

"Come, Speedy! Stand up!" he called. But the dog did not move.

Puzzled and upset, Ben-Zion slowly walked home, holding the dog in his arms.

Only in the evening, when his father had dug a hole in the garden and laid the cold body of the dog in it, did his tears begin to flow.

"Why did they do it to him?" he wept. "What did Speedy ever do to them? Why, Imma, why did they kill him?"

His mother stood beside him with young Avichayil in her arms. The baby could not grasp what had happened and kept calling the dog. "Peedy, Peedy, Peedy!"

"Why, Imma, why?"

"They were furious that you addressed the dog in Hebrew, the holy tongue. They considered it a sacrilege."

"But Imma, why?" Ben-Zion could not understand this. Tears kept flowing down his cheeks.

"Come, my son," said Eliezer gently. "Let us cover the dead dog with soil. Nobody is ever going to bother Speedy again."

Ben-Zion dug some soil with his bare hands, but when he was about to throw it on the dog, he discovered that he couldn't.

"I can't do it! I can't! It hurts me too much," he whimpered. "Please, Abba, don't do it!"

"I must, my child," said Eliezer. "Go and sit over there, and don't watch me. I will soon be finished."

Ben-Zion sat on the side, covered his face with his hands, and wept bitterly.

"Don't cry, my child," said Eliezer when he had finished his job.

Ben-Zion raised his eyes and saw a small mound of earth. This was all that was left of Speedy, his loyal friend.

"Now we'll place a stone on the grave. Come on, let's use this stone. What would you like me to inscribe on it?"

"Please, Abba, I would like you to write: 'Here lies Speedy Ben-Yehudah, a good dog who never harmed anybody. But he was killed by cruel children,' " said Ben-Zion, his voice breaking.

"No, I think I am going to write something different," said Eliezer. He began writing with a black lead pencil in block letters: "Here lies Speedy, the first Hebrew dog, who died defending the first Hebrew child." Then he placed the flat stone on the mound.

"Let's go home, son," said his mother, taking Ben-Zion's hand.

"You go. I want to sit here a little longer," said Ben-Zion as he squatted beside his dog's grave. He stayed there for a long time, until night covered the world with its dark cloak.

## * six

All week long Ben-Zion walked about gloomy and depressed. He did not play, touch his toys, talk, or laugh. He spent hours sitting, quiet and morose, near the mound in the garden. His parents tried to distract him—but the boy was inconsolable.

It was the eve of the last day of the Festival of Succot, the day of the Rejoicing of the Law. Jews could be seen hurrying to synagogue in the alleys of Jerusalem. Ben-Zion looked at the well-dressed children with flags in their hands, and there was sadness in his eyes.

"Would you care to come to synagogue with me?" suggested Eliezer. "It's lovely there tonight. You will see men dance with the scrolls of the Torah in their hands, singing and praying." Eliezer rarely went to synagogue, nor did he take his son out; but on this occasion he decided to do so, to console the boy and make him forget his sorrow.

Ben-Zion's sad eyes lit up. "We can really go to synagogue?"

"Yes, son. Come on, your mother will help you get

into your best clothes, and I will quickly make a small flag for you."

Dvorah dressed Ben-Zion in his bright cossack costume, which his grandparents had sent from Russia: a red shirt with flowing ribbons, and a pair of real breeches, like those of a genuine horseman. She helped him with his new shoes, combed his fair hair, and placed a nice red tarbush on his head. The child was delighted. When his father handed him his flag, which bore the inscription THE FLAG OF THE CAMP OF JUDAH OF THE ARMY OF ISRAEL, he was thrilled.

Father and son walked hand in hand. That evening Abba was not busy, and he was also not cross. This was not the Abba of the newspaper, who must never be disturbed. This time it was a real Abba, like the one Ben-Zion always longed for: pleasant, patient, and free.

The synagogue was lit up and filled with people. A crowd gathered around Ben-Zion. People who were complete. strangers to him came over, hugged and kissed him, gave him candy, and invited him to visit their homes.

"Tell me, Ben-Zion," asked one man, "Do you speak any Russian? You can come and visit us. I have five children who would be delighted to make friends with you."

"Let your children learn Hebrew, and then I will be delighted to ask them over to visit us," replied Eliezer, dragging his son away from the man.

The boy went around the synagogue like a sleepwalker. He went over to the holy ark and saw the Torah scrolls, which were wrapped in bright silk cloths. He joined the dancers and raised his flag high over his head. He was surrounded by love, warmth, and admiration.

"Abba, everybody here loves us, don't they?" he said to his father with sparkling eyes. "These people will never call us names and say we are crazy. I really think so." The lonely child, who was always starved for companionship, suddenly found himself surrounded by many people; what was even more wonderful, his father was affectionate and paid attention to him. Ben-Zion was a very happy boy that evening.

It was dark outside when they left the synagogue. They walked through the winding lanes of Jerusalem. A cold wind had started to blow, and dark clouds had gathered in the sky. From time to time a flash of lightning pierced the darkness.

"I am cold, Abba," said Ben-Zion. His teeth chattered.

"We'll soon be home," his father replied. "It will be warm inside. With luck, Ben-Zion, it may rain tonight. Everybody is expecting the rain and looks forward to it. Look, Ben-Zion, do you see this? All the people have put out their jars and pails to collect the rainwater." Eliezer pointed at the walls of the buildings. All sizes and shapes of pottery jars stood next to the walls.

They hurried home. Just as they were about to enter the gate, they noticed Dvorah sitting in the street on a broken box. Little Avichayil was in her arms, and various household articles were strewn about her.

"What's this? What has happened?" shouted Eliezer and ran toward his wife. They could make out the furious words of their landlord as he screamed at Dvorah. "You haven't paid your rent for six months.

*Ben-Zion at the age of four, holding a flag with the inscription* THE
FLAG OF THE CAMP OF JUDAH OF THE ARMY OF ISRAEL *(about 1885)*

*Ben-Zion and his sister Yemima*

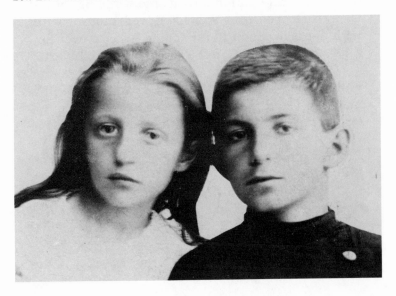

I have been patient and did not complain and never pressed you. Then your husband can turn around and do this to me. He wants water, does he? Well and good, he can have water tonight. Straight from heaven. He can have as much rain as he wants. Free of charge." Dvorah made no reply. She sat on the box, hugging the shivering child. Her eyes were bright with tears.

"What happened?" asked Eliezer.

"Oh, so he is here too, is he?" The landlord turned on Eliezer. "This is a fine way to show me your gratitude."

"What on earth are you talking about?" Eliezer was unable to understand.

"Your article. The article which you published in the paper. You wrote about the landlords with water in their wells who are praying for drought so that they can continue to rob the poor and charge them high prices for drinking water. You wrote this article about me! I am truly grateful to you!" he spat out as he turned away in a fury. The family remained in the street. It was dark. Rain had begun falling gently, then the gentle patter turned into a raging torrent. Dvorah stooped over Avichayil and protected him with her body, and Eliezer spread his coat over Ben-Zion's head. They sat in the street, wet and shivering.

"It's raining. There will be no drought," murmured Eliezer. "The jars will fill up and there will be plenty of water for everyone. Plenty of drinking water, plenty for the herds, for the fields, for the vineyards."

"I want to go home," whimpered Ben-Zion. "I am cold, Abba."

The rain kept falling for a long time. When it ceased, everybody went outside to collect the jars which had filled with water. The news that Ben-Yehudah and his family were sitting outside in the rain spread like wildfire. People turned up from all corners of Jerusalem.

"Thank you for bringing us rain, Ben-Yehudah," said an old man as he shook Eliezer's hand. He was convinced that Ben-Yehudah was personally responsible for the miracle.

"Poor children," cried a generous woman, "do come into my house."

"No, come over to my place," said someone else.

"Jews," shouted somebody. "Don't let this cruel landlord throw this family out of their home."

Fists banged on the iron gate. "So you throw children out in the rain, do you?"

"You leech, you bloodsucking leech!"

"You are a wicked man!"

"Your heart is made of stone!"

The landlord was afraid to leave his house. He sent a messenger to let the Ben-Yehudahs know that they could now return home.

The family entered the house, shivering and cold. Their clothes were soaked, and water dripped from all their belongings. Dvorah put her children to sleep and covered them with damp rags to warm them.

"Imma, I am cold and hungry," wept little Ben-Zion. All his joy and happiness had vanished. Now he could feel not only the bitter cold, but a gnawing hunger, too.

"There is no food in the house," murmured Dvorah apologetically. "Our last loaf of bread was soaked. Try to go to sleep, child. Imma will sing you to sleep." Dvorah sat down at her sons' bedsides and sang them a lovely lullaby. Finally, they fell asleep.

Dvorah rose and turned to her husband. As usual, he was standing by his tall desk, writing.

"Eliezer," she addressed him, "what are we going to do? We have no bread in the house, and the grocer won't let me have anything on credit. What shall we do?"

"I do not know, " replied Eliezer, raising his eyes and sighing deeply. "And things are going to get worse. I was informed today that I cannot continue teaching any longer."

"But why?" asked Dvorah. "You are a good teacher."

"So I am. There were no complaints about my work, or at least nobody mentioned any. But I am afraid they are not too keen on children speaking fluent Hebrew."

"Is that what they told you?"

"No. The excuse they gave was my health. They said it was not advisable for children to be in the company of a man who coughs constantly. From now on we shall have to manage on the profits from the newspaper."

"That's impossible. We can't do it," said Dvorah. "The money isn't enough for food—and where shall we get money for rent and to pay off some of our debts to the grocer?"

"I don't know what to do," said Eliezer. A note of despair crept into his voice.

"I do," said Dvorah. "You must go to Russia and ask my family to help us. I am sure they will."

Eliezer's eyes lit up. "That is an idea. Then I will be able to advocate my cause to the public. I may even find people to back my paper and help me publish a Hebrew dictionary."

"I am convinced that everybody who hears of your plans for the revival of the Hebrew language will assist you," said Dvorah.

"I wish I had your confidence," said Eliezer.

"You must go, darling," she begged.

"What will you do while I am away? Will you have the strength to keep my children from speaking foreign languages? Will you be able to continue with my work while I am abroad?"

"I swear that we shall only speak Hebrew at home."

"But you are pregnant. How are you going to manage?"

"Don't worry about me, Eliezer. As soon as the baby is born, I shall go and look for a job. I will have no difficulty obtaining a teaching post in a girls' school. Don't worry, Eliezer."

"I think I will do as you suggest," said Eliezer. "I shall leave as soon as the baby is born. Let us hope that I find new subscribers for the paper and backers for the dictionary. I do not want to leave you. But I have no choice."

## * *seven*

When Ben-Zion woke up in the morning, he was amazed to hear strange voices in the house. He jumped out of bed and ran to his parents' bedroom.

Behind the door he could make out loud female voices, then the sound of a sigh, which was followed by a louder sigh. "Where is Imma? What has happened to her?" he demanded. He tried to open the door, but found it locked. He could hear stifled groans.

"Imma!" he cried desperately and knocked on the door. "I want my Imma. What has happened to my Imma?" Suddenly he was overcome by a terrible fear. Then the door opened slowly, and Simcha, the widow who lived next door, was standing in the doorway. She had black hair and black eyes, and rolled her words in her mouth, so that they sounded very funny. She smiled at Ben-Zion, showing two rows of pearly teeth, and said, "Ben-Zion darling. Congratulations. You now have a baby sister. You may soon go inside and see her."

"I want to see her now. Let me come in. What has happened to my Imma? Where is she?" He tried squirming into the room, but Simcha's hefty figure blocked the way.

"Wait a little, Ben-Zion. The baby must first be washed and dressed nicely for such an important visitor as you."

"But what has happened to my Imma?" Ben-Zion was not at all interested in his sister just then.

"Your mother has just given birth to a baby. She had a difficult time and must rest."

"That's not true. She has no baby. Imma told me that the baby is not due yet. She said the baby would be born later. Why don't you let me go into the room?"

"That's right. The baby was expected in two months, but she did not want to wait. She heard all the excitement around here yesterday and decided to

have a look at this interesting world. Can you understand this, Ben-Zion?"

"No," said the child.

"Listen, darling, you will soon see your mother
and your sister. I will call you when they are ready."
She turned her back on him and locked the door behind her.

Ben-Zion remained sitting on the threshold, his
back to the locked door, and waited impatiently. He
could not make up his mind whether he like the idea
of a sister, or whether he resented her arrival. Now
Imma would be busier than ever and would have no
time at all for him. From behind the locked door he
heard a faint cry, and suddenly his heart was filled
with love and pity for the poor little creature crying
inside. He was suddenly happy. Now he had both a
brother and a tiny new sister. The noise made by the
baby was strange. It sounded like a mewing kitten. He
got up and ran over to the sleeping Avichayil.

"Avichayil, wake up, sleepyhead," he cried, shaking his brother, who was lying curled up on the bed.
"We have a sister." But Avichayil seemed indifferent
to the news. He blinked at Ben-Zion, turned his back
to him, and went back to sleep.

He doesn't understand a thing, thought Ben-Zion.
When I was a small boy and my brother was born, I
also could not understand a thing. Still, he desperately wanted to tell the good news to somebody. The
door to the yard was locked as usual. He stood at the
window. There were people in the street below: drivers with their donkeys, milkmen calling out; everybody seemed to be hurrying to work. "I have a sister!
I have a new sister!" the boy kept shouting. Nobody

had any time for the child, and his voice was lost in the general din of the street.

Suddenly he noticed his father riding on his small donkey. "Abba," he screamed at the top of his voice, "Abba, we have a new sister!"

The father was lost in thought and paid no attention to the shouting child. He approached the gate slowly. Ben-Zion heard him get off the donkey, tie it to the post, and climb heavily up the stairs.

"Abba, Abba, we now have a small sister!" cried Ben-Zion as he ran to meet him.

"Is that so? I am truly delighted," said the father cheerfully as he picked up some papers from his desk and turned away.

"Abba, we'll soon be able to see her. Wait a second."

"I have no time," said Eliezer, buttoning his jacket. "I will see her this evening. And your job will be to make sure that nobody speaks anything but Hebrew near the baby." Having uttered these words he left the house.

Sometimes I get the feeling that Abba loves Hebrew more than he loves us, the indignant and hurt Ben-Zion thought. He went back to his mother's room and listened at the door.

Finally it opened, and Simcha, with a sweeping gesture and a wide grin, invited Ben-Zion to enter. The room was dark. The windows were shut, and a strange smell hung in the air. For a moment the child was scared and wanted to leave.

"Ben-Zion, my son, come over here." He could barely make out his mother's weak voice.

He went over to the large bed. His mother was

covered by a sheet, her face very pale, her hair glistening with sweat. Her lips seemed strangely dark. A small parcel, wrapped in a piece of colored cloth, lay next to her.

"Here, Ben-Zion. Have a look. This is your new sister. Do you like her?"

Ben-Zion took one look at the small creature: a miniature baby with a reddish face, light hair, eyes that were puffed and closed, and a tiny nose.

"She is very pretty. So cute!" exclaimed Ben-Zion after studying her carefully. "What will you call her?"

"We thought of Yemima. What do you think of that name, darling?" Dvorah smiled wearily.

"I think Yemima is a lovely name." The baby seemed so tiny and helpless. Once again his heart was flooded with love and pity.

Simcha picked the baby up in her arms and began to croon a lullaby in Arabic. Ben-Zion rose angrily from his chair. "She must not hear a foreign language! You must stop."

"Just look at him! So now we have another policeman around here," smiled Chaya-Leah, the tea-vendor, who was busy cleaning the room. "I still remember the day this little Ben-Zion was born," she said as she walked over to the bed. "Remember, Dvorah? You let me pick him up, but I was not allowed to open my mouth. I did not speak a word of Hebrew at the time, and his father objected to anybody speaking any other language in his presence from the moment he was born."

"You have certainly picked up some Hebrew over the years," remarked Dvorah.

"What else could I do? Ben-Zion was like my own flesh and blood, and I wanted to speak to him. You see, dear, I learned to speak Hebrew for your sake. And now you are standing over me, making sure that I do not contaminate your sister's ears with a foreign language."

"Five years ago you were born," said Simcha. "But it seems like only yesterday. You were very tiny. No bigger than Yemima."

"I was never so small," objected Ben-Zion. "Right, Imma?"

"No, not quite so small," said his mother. "Still, you were pretty small."

"But I was never *so* small, was I, Imma?" Ben-Zion insisted.

Bracha, the midwife, did not speak a word of Hebrew. She entered the room with a steaming cup of tea for Dvorah. She agreed to Dvorah's insistence that she should not speak a foreign language in the children's presence, so she gestured to Dvorah in sign language and pantomime. Ben-Zion could not help himself and burst out laughing at this sight. Bracha gave him a stern glance and made a sign of annoyance with her finger.

He looked away and leaned over the baby.

"May I touch her, Imma?" he asked.

"Yes, my dear. But be very careful."

He put out his finger and touched the baby's small hand gingerly.

"Look, Imma! Look at these tiny fingers. Look! She has five fingers on each hand. She even has fingernails," he said in amazement. "She's so cute. Now I have a brother and a sister, and so has Avichayil.

Only Yemima has no sister. She has two brothers. Do you think she minds?"

"You wait long enough, and your mother will attend to this, too," said Simcha. "She will bring you another sister, and then Yemima will also have a sister."

Ben-Zion wished all these women would go away. He wanted to remain alone with little Yemima and his mother. But the women kept moving around the room, acting as if they were in their own homes, and Ben-Zion decided to ignore them. He turned his back on them and sat next to his mother, one hand flung around her neck, the other stroking the baby tenderly.

"Yemima my sweet, Yemima my darling," he whispered.

Dvorah watched him, and her eyes brimmed with love. "Do you really love her, my child?" she asked.

"I do. I love her very much. I even love her more than I love dogs. Now I'll even forget about Speedy. Do you think I will, Imma?"

## * *eight*

Ben-Zion's love for little Yemima grew from day to day. He would spend hours sitting near her cot and watching over her.

"Imma," he would run over and inform Dvorah,

"she has just opened her eyes. Look, she stretches her hand! Oh, Imma, she can see me! She already loves me, doesn't she? Listen! She actually laughed in Hebrew!" Ben-Zion was very excited when he first heard the baby's gurgling laughter.

The children were a source of great happiness to Dvorah. But her happiness did not dispel their poverty. Eliezer worked day and night, but his hard work brought little food into the house. His paper was in debt; the meager income from subscriptions barely covered publication costs. Eliezer toured Jerusalem and the pioneer villages in the Judean Hills and the plain in search of new subscribers.

Many of the newly arrived young pioneers backed Ben-Yehudah's views—but they were poor and could not afford a subscription to a newspaper. The old-timers who lived in Jerusalem and Jaffa did not think much of the paper. The rabbis despised Ben-Yehudah and his strange ideas. They objected to his use of modern Hebrew and regarded him as an infidel for daring to use the holy tongue for everyday matters. They objected violently to the articles in his papers which advocated the return of Jews to farming or labor. They instructed their followers not to subscribe to the paper. Many people dropped their subscriptions. The number of subscribers grew smaller each day. The expenses of the paper rose.

Ben-Yehudah tried his best to improve the paper, but there was no money at his disposal. He worked in the cellar of a house by the light of a kerosene lamp. Every letter had to be set by hand.

At first he gave this job to qualified typesetters, but when he realized that there too many printing errors in his paper, he undertook this task himself. And so it came about that Ben-Yehudah did all the work on the newspaper. He wrote the articles, set the letters, typed, and read proofs; when the paper was printed, he took the copies home, folded them, stamped them, went to the post office, and mailed them to subscribers. The paper came out on Fridays, and Eliezer worked very hard all week in order to make the deadline. When he came home at night, he would continue to work on his Hebrew dictionary—standing at his tall desk.

The family went hungry. Dvorah learned to sew and embroider from her Sephardic neighbors, and at night, when the children were asleep, she would bend over a kerosene lamp and embroider. The few pennies which she earned with her work went to buy flour and oil. This was their main meal for many months. The children would dip the black bread which she baked in the oven in the courtyard into the oil which she bought from vendors who came to the house on their donkeys. Eliezer was the only one who ate properly; Dvorah and the children ate very frugally so as to be able to buy him an occasional piece of meat and some milk, for he was unwell and she worried about him. His cough had grown worse, and working by the light of the kerosene lamp had made his eyes red and swollen. He breathed with great difficulty and often coughed up blood.

Dvorah used to wait for him to come home from

the printing press, set the table for him, and leave the room in a hurry.

"Why don't you eat with me?" he would ask her angrily. "You know I don't like eating alone."

"I can't wait for you. I get hungry much earlier," she lied to him as she went out of the room. She was afraid to stay in the room lest her eyes betray her at the sight of the food. The children were also continuously hungry. The oil-dipped bread was hardly enough to sustain them. Ben-Zion and Avichayil often went to sleep with empty stomachs, tears of gnawing hunger in their eyes.

"I am hungry, Imma. Let me have something to eat. Give me just one more slice of bread," they kept begging all day long.

Even little Yemima began to show signs of hunger. From day to day Dvorah's milk dwindled, and the hunger cries of the baby could be heard all over the house.

Eliezer did not realize what was going on in the house. He was totally immersed in his affairs, and Dvorah did not want to complain. After all, there was very little he could do to change the situation. She became thin and haggard, and after a while was racked by coughing. But when the children began to cough, too, she saw no alternative, and once again suggested that Eliezer go to Russia, to her family, and ask for their assistance. "Take a loan and go abroad," she said. "We are in a very bad way. The children are hungry, they have no warm clothes for winter, we have many debts, and we have nothing in the house to sell anymore. I am going to get a job as a French teacher in the Girls' School."

"What will you do with the children when you are at work?"

"I will take Avichayil and Yemima to work with me. Ben-Zion can go to school."

"Never!" screamed Eliezer. "I have vowed that my eldest son will not be under any outside influences. I will not send him to school, where French is the main language, and destroy all the labor of these last few years. And you are not going to take the children outside to the street and expose them to foreign languages."

Days passed. Dvorah did not bring up the subject again. She would go around for days without speaking at all. The only sound in the house was the sound of hungry children. It was a terrifying sound—a hunger cry mingled with coughing. The children were pale; their faces became gaunt. The happy baby no longer laughed. She would lie on her cot, staring up with enormous sad eyes.

Finally, Eliezer could no longer endure the situation. "All right, Dvorah," he told her one evening. "I am going to go to Russia. But I want you to promise that when you take the children to school with you, you will never let anybody who does not speak Hebrew address them. They must completely isolated during your working hours."

Dvorah promised to do as he bade her.

Next morning Eliezer began to prepare for his journey, and Dvorah with her three children set off to the Girls' School. Near the school building stood a small, dusty, mildewed storehouse, full of old books and ancient furniture. This was where she left her children. She placed the baby on a blanket which she spread out on an old couch, and told Ben-Zion and Avichayil to watch over her. Then she made sure that the door was locked. In the intervals between the lessons she hurried over to her children and took them some food. For a whole week the children spent seven hours a day in the dark storehouse.

"Imma," Ben-Zion asked her one day, "why do you lock us up?"

"I don't want anyone to steal you," she replied, trying to turn the whole issue into a joke.

"What? Do you mean to say that people who speak no Hebrew steal children?" asked the child.

"No, darling," the mother replied.

"What a shame." Ben-Zion was genuinely sorry. "I wish someone *would* steal me. If someone would steal me, I could go outside for a walk and make friends. Would you mind very much if I were stolen?"

"Yes, dearest. I would miss you terribly."

"But I shall come and visit you from time to time. You will not be able to recognize me after so many years, but I shall come back and whisper to you, 'It's me. Your son, Ben-Zion!' Then I would show you the little mole under my right arm and you would know that it really is me. But I am not going to tell Abba that it's me, because he is sure to be angry. I will come to you alone and kiss you and go back to being stolen. Oh, Imma! I so much want to be stolen!"

Dvorah's eyes filled with tears. At night she told Eliezer of Ben-Zion's wish. "Can you understand this, my husband? The child is so miserable and lonely that he hopes and dreams of being stolen. He will hate us the rest of his life for turning his childhood into a prison. We can't do this to him, Eliezer. His Hebrew will not be jeopardized. I will make sure I speak only Hebrew with the children when I return from school. Please let Ben-Zion go to school."

Eliezer turned a stubborn back on Dvorah and went on writing as though he had not heard her.

The next day the family accompanied the father to the carriage which was to take him from Jerusalem to the port of Jaffa. Dvorah held little Yemima in her arms, Eliezer walked at her side, and Avichayil walked between them. Ben-Zion marched in front of the family, glowing with pleasure at the outing. He looked at everybody in the street, and his eyes shone.

"Will you let me send him to school?" Dvorah tried again.

"He is too young. He is only five years old, and the boys in the first grade are six or seven," the father replied.

"Don't let that worry you. He is well ahead of his age and is sure to pick up reading and writing very quickly. I seem to remember that you began learning at heder at the age of four, didn't you?"

"So I did. But I learned in Yiddish, which was a language I knew. He will have to go to a school where everything is taught in French, and it will make things very difficult for him. What's more, his Hebrew will be spoiled."

"I doubt it," said Dvorah. She could feel Eliezer beginning to give in a little. "He speaks Hebrew fluently, and no other language can really replace it.

And after all, they do teach some Hebrew at the French School."

"I don't think much of it," said Eliezer, and fell silent. They reached the carriage. Eliezer climbed up and settled inside.

"Good-bye, Abba," the children called, waving their hands.

"Good-bye, my husband, and take care," Dvorah said, trying hard to swallow the tears which were choking her.

"G'bye, g'bye." The baby tried to wave her hand, too.

"Good-bye, my children. Good-bye, Dvorah!" Eliezer seemed very stern.

The carriage began to move.

"Abba! Take me along with you!" burst out Ben-Zion. "I want to go away from here. I want to be stolen and taken away. Please, please, Abba!"

Dvorah could no longer contain herself. Her lips quivered and tears began to flow down her cheeks.

"All right! Send him!" she heard her husband's voice shout from within the carriage. "Let him start school tomorrow."

"Ben-Zion," she called to the child, who was running after the carriage. "Come back, Ben-Zion. Come here, darling. I have such lovely news for you." Ben-Zion walked back to her with obvious reluctance.

"You are going to start school tomorrow. You will learn to read and write. You will be able to play with other children. You are going to have friends, Ben-Zion darling."

"To school? I will really go to a classroom? You are not going to lock me up in the old storehouse anymore?" Ben-Zion could hardly contain his excitement. "Oh, Imma! You are so good to me! I am so happy!"

## * *nine*

Ben-Zion eventually grew accustomed to school, but he never learned to enjoy it. He preferred being locked up in the cobbled yard at home. There the bright sun shone upon him and the air was sweet and fresh. At least in the yard he could look out into the street and daydream, but here in school he had to watch the teacher and pay attention to what was being said. And Ben-Zion found it difficult to concentrate when everybody spoke in a strange language. What was the point of repeating the teacher's words like a parrot—without understanding what was being said?

Ben-Zion found the first few weeks at school extremely difficult. But soon his vocabulary grew and he began to understand and absorb what was being said. His teachers praised him for his stubbornness and hard work, but his classmates did not like him. During recesses, they would surround him and insist that he answer them in their respective languages. They spoke many different languages: Russian, French, German, Polish, and Yiddish—languages spoken by Jews who had come to the land of Israel from all over the world. He would stand silent among the boys, and they would call him names, like idiot, dumb, stupid. There were even times when they bullied him and beat him up.

He tried desperately to win their affection. He gave them gifts. He handed out all his meager possessions. He gave a pencil to one boy, a sheet of paper to another, and part of his lunch to a third boy—although the meal was hardly enough for one.

When he returned home without his belongings, and as hungry as a wolf, Dvorah would be furious. "Where is your pencil, Ben-Zion? And what is this? I gave you a new handkerchief this morning? What have you done with it? You mean to say you are hungry? Why didn't you have lunch at school?"

When people told her what was happening, she became livid. "Why do you have to go around sharing everything? If your father were here he would punish you for this."

"I don't share everything," he would defend himself. "I lose things."

"Just by looking at you I can tell you are lying. You don't just lose things all the time. You share everything you have, even your lunches, with the other children. Why do you do this, Ben-Zion?"

"I want to have least one friend," he told her. "Everybody else has friends. I am the only boy who has no friends. I give them things to make them want to be friends with me. Do you think they will ever be my friends, Imma?"

Dvorah's eyes brimmed with tears as she looked at her son. Her heart cringed with pity and pain for her child who was trying so desperately to buy friendship and affection with a pencil, a handkerchief, or a sandwich.

One day Ben-Zion was sitting in the classroom during an arithmetic lesson. This was a lesson he detested. The teacher was a short man with a monotonous voice. Ben-Zion had not yet learned the figures and arithmetic signs in French and was very bored. He shut his eyes and dozed. Suddenly he woke in a panic to the sound of raucous laughter. He turned to the other boys in the class, trying to figure out what had happened. He noticed that even the teacher smirked.

Then he realized what had happened. There was a small puddle under his seat. His pants were wet. He had had an accident in his sleep. The shame seemed immense. He could not stay in the classroom. He rose from his seat, hurried to the door, and ran down the corridor. He was followed by sounds of laughter and jeering. He went out the school gate and ran up the street. He crossed roads and ran through winding lanes until he reached his home. The door was locked. Wet and ashamed, he curled up on the threshold, trying to hide from neighbors and passersby, to wait for his mother.

In the evening, when Dvorah returned home, she found her son shivering with cold, his eyes red from weeping. "I will never go back to that school," he told her, and began to cry again. "They always laugh at me. Now they will never let me forget this."

Dvorah tried to persuade him to return, but Ben-Zion was stubborn. For a week he stayed home and refused to go back to school. He even dreaded going out to the street, in case he met someone who had heard of his "accident."

Dvorah did not know what to do. Had her husband been home he would simply have ordered his son to return to school. But she could not do it. She was hurt by her son's agony and could not help him in his trouble.

One day, on her way to the Girls' School, she went in to see Mr. Bechar, the headmaster. The friendly man listened to her story and that very afternoon made it his business to drop in and see them. "Well, Ben-Zion, are you sick or something? Why don't you go to school?" He pretended to know nothing of the incident.

"I don't want to go to school anymore," Ben-Zion replied sulkily.

"Why not?"

"The boys don't like me. They laugh at me and . . ." He hesitated.

"Oh, you must be referring to the thing which happened to you the other day? I know all about that," he added softly. "Do you know something, the very same thing happened to me when I was much older than you are now. It happened because I was weak and very tired. You must make sure you go to bed in time and eat all your meals properly. I can assure you that such a thing will never happen to you again. You have proved that you are a good pupil, and I have been thinking of transferring you to a higher grade, anyhow. Would you like that, Ben-Zion?"

It took Mr. Bechar an entire evening to persuade Ben-Zion to return to school.

When Ben-Zion went through the school gate the next morning, he felt awkward and embarrassed. His eyes were downcast, and he was all set to flee if anybody laughed at him. To his relief, nobody ever mentioned the incident again—probably because Mr. Bechar had warned the children not to. He began to study in the second grade, and after a while practically forgot the entire affair.

He felt much more at ease with the older boys. He still lagged behind with his studies, but he already had the reputation of a boy who knows a great deal about general matters. At home he listened to adult conversations and learned about politics and newspapers. He knew the names of many countries from the pictures he saw at home and liked telling his classmates about them. His biblical interpretations were particularly brilliant. He loved the Bible stories and had his own explanations for the names of the heroes.

"Eglon, king of Moab? Why, he must have been called Eglon—coachman—because he was as big and fat as the largest and most important coachman in Moab."

"Ehud, son of Gera? He was named Ehud—beloved—because he must have been very popular." At the time, he did not know that this word was another one of his father's innovations.

"Dvorah—bee—the woman of Lapidoth, was the queen of the bees. She was not afraid of bees because she used to carry a torch—*lapid*—in her hand, and you all know that bees dislike fire and smoke."

Ben-Zion's horizon grew from day to day. But he did not speak much Hebrew, except when he returned from school in the evening. During the day he spoke two or three languages, brokenly, and when he ran out of words, he used sign language.

Dvorah was very strict about speaking Hebrew at home. And when Eliezer returned from his trip a few months later, he discovered that Ben-Zion could read and write and had learned some arithmetic. He also noticed that his son's Hebrew was as good as it had been before he had left. This encouraged Eliezer a little. He had returned very depressed from his trip, which had been a failure. He had succeeded in finding only a handful of new subscribers for the paper. People refused to back him, and many tried to dissuade him from this "madness"—the revival of a dead language in a backward country in the Middle East.

So Ben-Yehudah, who had come back sad and dejected, at least saw some reward for his labor. His eldest son was doing well at school. His Hebrew was not only unaffected by the influence of other children in the class, but it had also served to make his world richer and wider. When Eliezer realized this, he decided the time had come to send Avichayil to school.

So now they were two against the school: Ben-Zion and Avichayil. Ben-Zion was no longer lonely. Avichayil did not try to make friends through gifts of food and pencils. Although Avichayil was small and puny, he was extremely strong and would beat up anyone who tried teasing him. The father insisted that they speak only Hebrew during recess. Other children occasionally listened in to their conversations and even tried to join them. Ben-Zion began to become popular with both teachers and pupils.

Ben-Zion dislike his Turkish master most of all. This was a teacher who had his own unique teaching method. He believed that the more you beat a child, the clearer his head becomes for studies. He beat children for no reason and occasionally broke his cane on some unfortunate child's back. One day, during the weekly Turkish lesson, Ben-Zion whispered to his friends, "Teacher's voice twangs like his cane." The boys burst out laughing.

"What did you say?" asked the teacher as he approached Ben-Zion with his cane in hand.

"I said that you have a powerful cane as well as a powerful voice," replied Ben-Zion bravely. A murmur of admiration went through the classroom.

"Stand up, Ben-Zion," thundered the terrible voice. The cane was raised.

"You just dare to hit me! My father will write about you in his paper!" Ben-Zion shouted in defiance.

"The devil take your father and his paper!" roared the teacher, as he struck Ben-Zion's head, back, arms, and legs. The boys were furious. Ben-Zion's scream of terror and pain mingled with the teacher's shouts of anger. "I will kill you, you loud-mouth!" and a hail of blows followed. "How dare you speak to me like this, you spoiled brat! I will show you the meaning of a newspaper. I will teach you how to write in a paper!"

Mr. Bechar, the headmaster, heard the shouting and rushed to the classroom. He tore the boy from the hands of the teacher, who had gone wild.

"I will never come back to this school," Ben-Zion said. "I've had enough!"

"I am going to try something else, Ben-Zion," Mr. Bechar told him gently. "You will go up to the third

grade. The Turkish master does not teach that class.
I hope this will end your trouble in our school. Three
grades in a single year are quite enough!"

## * *ten*

New and wonderful worlds opened up before Ben-
Zion in the third grade. They read books and discussed distant lands and strange cultures. Everything
was taught in French.

Ben-Yehudah resented this state of affairs and
did everything in his power to revive Hebrew and
Hebrew subjects. But nobody listened to his arguments.

"This is a French school," the principal replied
dryly. "It is attended by Jews, Moslems, and Chris-
tians. French is the official language of the school.
There are also Turkish, Arabic, and a little Hebrew—
but only because the school is located in Jerusalem."

Ben-Yehudah was furious, but there was nothing
he could do.

"Don't worry about Ben-Zion," Dvorah tried to
calm her husband. "He speaks fluent Hebrew. And
besides, no other school teaches any more Hebrew."

"I know that. And it is very sad," replied Eliezer.

Ben-Zion was enchanted by the charm and rich-
ness of the French language. New horizons opened
up before him, disclosing a wonderful culture. The
language formed a bridge between him and the other

children. Now that they could talk to him, he was accepted by the others and could mix with them; he did not feel like a lonely stranger. The third grade had excellent teachers; they taught him to love the new language.

"Do you and Avichayil make sure you speak only Hebrew during recess?" Eliezer kept asking sternly.

"Usually we do," replied Ben-Zion, lowering his eyes.

"You must keep it up!" the father insisted.

"It is not always so easy, Abba," explained Ben-Zion. "We are not in the same class, and we each have our own friends. We don't always see each other during recess."

"Then you must leave your friends and go and seek your brother out. And the same goes for you, Avichayil. Or speak Hebrew with your friends. Are you listening, Avichayil?"

"But—" Avichayil began to protest.

"I know it's not going to be easy. But you must do it!"

Indeed, it was not at all easy. The brothers tried to avoid each other during the recess periods so as not to speak Hebrew and feel themselves outside their circle of friends. They realized that they were unable to carry out their father's strict orders, and could not speak to their friends in Hebrew. There was nobody who was willing to make the effort to speak this difficult language. Sometimes Ben-Zion was furious with his father. What did he want? Why couldn't he leave him alone? Why couldn't he be like all the other fathers? For Ben-Zion, Hebrew had come to symbolize his father's tyranny, and he tried to break away from it.

It was so different with the French language. No-body made him speak French. On the contrary, he was only praised for speaking it. The other children, who spoke a mixture of languages, were not always very particular with their French. For Ben-Zion, this was the only language through which he could communicate with his friends, and he regarded French as the anchor in his sea of loneliness. He clung to it and progressed.

One day the French master said to him, "Ben-Zion, come over to my room at eight o'clock this evening. I live in the courtyard of the Sephardi Synagogue. I would very much like you to come, because there is something I want to give you."

"What is it?" asked Ben-Zion.

"If you come this evening you will find out for yourself," said the teacher with a smile.

All day long Ben-Zion waited for the evening. When darkness came he slipped out of the house silently and ran with his heart in his mouth till he reached the Sephardi Synagogue. He entered the courtyard and knocked on the door.

"You are slightly early, Ben-Zion," greeted the teacher. "Do come in."

Ben-Zion entered the room and looked around. The room was very small and was almost without furniture. Stacks of books covered most of the floor and filled the desk and the bed. There were books everywhere.

"Do you see these books?" asked the teacher, pointing with his finger. "They are all in French. They contain stories, poems, plays, science. . . . I want you to start reading. Your French is adequate."

Ben-Zion stared at the pile of books. "My father also has many books," he said, "but they are not just in French. He has books in many different languages. But . . ." he hesitated. What if the teacher discovered that his father objected to his reading anything but Hebrew? Perhaps he would not let him read any of these books.

"Here, take this book," said the teacher as he picked a thick book out of one of the piles, a book with a picture of a large ship on its cover. "It is called *Around the World in Eighty Days* and was written by Jules Verne. It is a very interesting book. Take it home with you. When you finish it, bring it back to me. We'll discuss it, and then I will give you another book. Are you interested in this arrangement, Ben-Zion?"

"Thank you very much," replied the boy. He opened the book. The print was very clear, and the pictures were large and colorful. His eyes roamed over the sentences. The book was fascinating right from the very beginning. It was so gripping that Ben-Zion forgot himself and did not realize that he was still standing and reading the book in his teacher's home.

"I knew you would like it," said the teacher, happy to see the boy's eagerness, "But it is time for you to go home now. It is late. When you finish the book, come back to me, and if you understand what it is all about, I will let you have another book."

Nobody had to remind Ben-Zion to go to bed that evening. He clasped the book and lay in his bed, trying to guess whether the hero of his book could possibly win his bet. Would he be able to travel around the world in eighty days? As soon as there was silence in the house and everybody had gone to sleep, Ben-Zion left his bed, walked barefoot on tiptoe to the small window, and pulled the curtain to one side. The lantern light flooded his father's tall desk. Ben-Zion held the book so the light could fall on it and started to read. He read for a long time, until his feet hurt and his eyes were bleary. Then he returned to his bed, with the book at his side, and fell fast asleep.

The next day he took the book to school with him. Every now and then he would peep at it; but he was afraid that his teacher would see him and stop lending him books. He waited impatiently for the lunch hour, and then sat in a corner and read the book. When he returned home, he found a hidden nook where nobody would bother him and went on reading. He was so engrossed in the book that he did not notice his father, who had entered the room and was towering over him.

"What are you reading?" asked Eliezer, as he took the book from his son's hands.

Ben-Zion jumped up in fright and was at a loss for words. Eliezer looked at the book and, to Ben-Zion's surprise, was not angry at all.

"This is a very good book, Ben-Zion," he told him, handing the book back. "I am about to translate it into Hebrew and publish it in installments in my paper. Don't bother reading it in French. Soon you will be able to read it in Hebrew."

"Yes, Abba," replied Ben-Zion quietly. But the temptation was too great, and he was unable to stop reading the book. He had already read some books that had been translated into Hebrew, and none of

*Eliezer Ben-Yehudah with Chemdah, his second wife (sister of Dvorah), resting under an olive tree on the outskirts of Jerusalem (about 1893)*

them had seemed as vivid and as flowing as this book. At that time the Hebrew used for translation was heavy, and lacked the vigor of a modern, spoken language. Ben-Zion found it difficult to understand why he had to read this awkward Hebrew, which was printed in small print on bad paper, without illustrations. Here was this lovely book, full of pictures, written in a beautiful language with large print intended for children. So he continued to read the book stealthily until he finished it. That evening he went again to his French master and asked for another book. He read many books secretly in French.

Ben-Yehudah was angry with his son for not being interested in the many adventure books which he translated for him. "Try this book," he would suggest, handing Ben-Zion a thin book bound in a gray cardboard. "It is a very interesting book. The beginning may be a bit difficult, but it gets easier as you go along."

Ben-Zion was not interested in reading his father's translations, which were filled with words he did not understand, words which his father had invented for the translation.

Eliezer was very disappointed in his son. "You should not be satisfied only with what you learn in school," he told him. "You can find the whole world in books. There are some beautiful stories which can teach you a great deal. You must read more."

Ben-Zion found it convenient to ignore these words and did not tell his father that he was reading books in French. Dvorah, who knew her son's secret, did not say a thing about it to her husband.

Eliezer's disappointment in his son increased

when at the end of the term the boy was first in his class in French and only second in Hebrew. Eliezer could not understand this at all. He watched his son angrily, but did not say a word. He did not speak to Ben-Zion all week long. When Ben-Zion tried to talk to him, he did not reply.

## * *eleven*

It was summer, a time of vacation from school, a time for roaming through the streets and alleys of Jerusalem. This vacation Ben-Zion was a happy boy. He could run and play in the open spaces, in the fresh air, like a bird escaping its cage. Avichayil and Ben-Zion roamed through the narrow, dirty alleys, played with dogs, caught rides on camels or donkeys, and enjoyed their freedom. Sometimes they would leave the city and play on Mount Zion, running up and down the hill. Then they would lie on the ground and look at the blue sky as they breathed the fresh mountain air. It was wonderful to be outside! No studies, no teachers, no dark, stifling classroom.

Eventually, Ben-Zion became bored with his vacation. He missed the company of other children. The teacher who owned the library had left town, and Ben-Zion had no books to read. So he wanted the company of his noisy and boisterous friends. The silence hemmed him in. Eliezer did not want his son to mix with children who spoke foreign languages. He was forced to accept the fact that Ben-Zion met those children in school, but he would not permit his sons to visit their friends during vacation; nor were they allowed to bring them home—unless they spoke only Hebrew. And nobody could do that. All the other children had plenty of friends and could easily do without the visit to the Ben-Yehudah home, to the "crazy fellow," as they called Eliezer. So the two boys found themselves without friends. Ben-Zion rebelled against his father's orders.

Dvorah would say to him, "Perhaps he'll permit you to play with the boys in spite of everything he says. Why don't you ask him nicely?"

"I know him. He will not agree. Particularly now that he is mad at me for coming out second in the class in Hebrew."

He found consolation in little Yemima. He loved her very much and spent many hours in her company, helping her to walk along the yard, shouting in delight whenever she came out with another one of her cute sentences. But even a sweet and adorable baby was no substitute for friends with whom it was possible to play.

One morning he went out of the house and saw some boys playing football in the next street. The boys were David and Reuven, his classmates; Nissim, who was from a higher grade; and Yitzhak, Marco, and Pierre, who were neighbors. Ben-Zion stood and watched them.

"Hey! Here is Ben-Zion," called David. "We're short a player. Want to join us?"

Ben-Zion ran over to them happily.

"It's no good playing here," said David. "There are too many stones in this street. Let's go and play in somebody's yard."

"We can go over to your place," suggested David. "It's the closest yard."

"Our yard?" said Ben-Zion, hesitating. What would his father say? Then he remembered that his father had gone off to work on his newspaper and that his mother would certainly have no objections.

"That's all right," he said. "But please, fellows, remember that you must speak Hebrew at our place."

"Fine," said Nissim in French. "We can play in Hebrew."

The children ran, skipping and jostling each other. In no time they were in the midst of a lively game. After a while they began to argue about the rules of the game. The argument turned into a heated discussion. They forgot about speaking Hebrew; it is impossible to fight and curse in anything but your mother tongue. The boys were fighting in Russian, Yiddish, and Arabic. Ben-Zion shouted louder than all the rest; he screamed in French. Soon a free-for-all broke out.

"That's enough!" thundered David. "We came here to play, not to fight." He spoke good French which everybody could understand. "Come on, let's make up. Each one must cross his hands and give them to the boys on either side of him. Now, as a signal for peace, let's sing the French national anthem, the *Marseillaise.* One, two, three, go!"

The boys held hands and sang loudly to celebrate the peace and brotherhood which would now reign among them forever.

Ben-Zion noticed his father only when he already stood on the threshold. Dressed in his Eastern costume with a tarbush on his head, Ben-Yehudah stood very still. His face was livid and his fists were clenched.

"He is here!" screamed Nissim, turning white.

"Run, run! The crazy fellow will kill you!" shouted another boy. The children ran for their lives.

"Crazy, crazy," sounded the voice from the street. "Ben-Yehudah the crazy! Yudke the infidel!" the children shouted from their safe positions across the fence. "A family of madmen! Yudke, Yudke! Yudke the infidel!"

Ben-Zion stood very still, shamed and frightened, and watched his father.

"Follow me," ordered his father, quietly. Ben-Zion followed him with shaking knees, the children's screams of derision still ringing in his ears. He hated each and every one of them. They had just sung the song of friendship together, and already they had betrayed him. They had left him and run away. And what was worse, they were rubbing salt into his wounds. He hated his father, too, the hard, harsh, tyrannical father. What was he going to do to him now? Was he going to beat him?

Ben-Yehudah went into the house, and Ben-Zion followed him. Ben-Yehudah removed his belt and began beating Ben-Zion wordlessly. Four lashes of the belt for each of the four verses of the song. Ben-Zion swallowed his tears. His body ached, but the insult and indignation were much more painful. His father turned and went out of the room without uttering a sound. His son was left sprawling on the floor, just barely controlling his tears.

Dvorah ran over to her son. She lifted him from the floor and stroked his burning back.

"You should not have done what you did, child. After all, you know—"

"Yes, I know!" Ben-Zion interrupted her. "I know just what sort of a father I have. But why, Imma? Why am I not allowed to do the things everybody else can do?" Now the tears began to flow freely from his eyes. "Why, Imma, why?"

"You are still too young to understand your father and his battle. One day you will realize what it is all about. You will be very proud of your father and proud of having been the first Hebrew child."

"I don't want to be the first Hebrew child," he wept. "I want to be like all other boys. I want my father to be like all other fathers. I want him to love me—"

"Oh, Ben-Zion, you are mistaken. Your father loves you very much. Don't ever doubt it. True, he is always busy, and he is very strict with you and concerned about your studies. But this is all because he loves you so much. When you were a baby he used to spend many hours reading Bible stories to you. He wanted your ears to get used to the sound of Hebrew. I will never forget," she added, "how he tried to make you stand up when you were only four months old. He told you to stand, in Hebrew, and to show you the meaning of the word he tried to help you stand up. He used to hold you in his arms and point at the furniture in the room and call them by name: 'This is a chair, this is a table, this is a window.' "

Ben-Zion always liked his mother's stories about his childhood, but today her stories could not make him forget his pain and hurt.

"I've heard those stories so many times! But I want a father like the other boys have. It hurts me that they call him crazy and laugh at him. They laugh at all of us. I don't want this!" he repeated as he burst into bitter tears.

## * twelve

The summer vacation ended, and Ben-Zion was eager to return to school. Ever since the *Marseillaise* incident he did not dare invite his friends over, nor did he go near them. On the first day of school he went off happily. In the distance he could make out the voices of the shouting children. He entered the vaulted gate and called out, "Hi, hi, everybody!"

Nobody greeted him. He was met by stony faces. Eyes stared through him, refusing to see him.

"David, David," he called to his closest friend. "What's up?"

"I'm sorry. I mustn't talk to you," replied David as he walked away.

"What do you mean?" Ben-Zion could not comprehend what was happening. "Is it because my father was mad at us? He's forgotten everything already. And anyhow, David, he wasn't mad at you, it was me he was mad at."

"That's not the reason. Please, Ben-Zion, don't speak to me again and don't embarrass me," said David. "I simply can't talk to you."

"But why?"

There was no response. David turned his back on his friend and walked off. Nobody spoke to him in the corridor, and everybody shied away from him as if he was disgusting and filthy. Ben-Zion was shocked. He sat in a corner of the classroom but was unable to concentrate. During the entire lesson he tried to puzzle out why the boys were behaving so strangely. Had he done anything to make them treat him this way? Even the teacher acted strangely—he did not address Ben-Zion or ask him any questions.

During the lunch hour he tried again. "David, please tell me what I've done. At least let me know the reason for all this." There were tears in his eyes.

"Just look over there, and you'll understand," said David curtly as he pointed with his finger to the wall across the road.

There was a large notice on the wall, written in Yiddish. Ben-Zion, who spoke no Yiddish, was unable to understand its contents. Then the name Ben-Yehudah sprang out in large, black letters. He guessed that the notice must contain some terrible message about his father. What happened? What did my father do? What is written up there?

Little Yitzhak volunteered the information. "Yesterday they lit black candles for your father, and at night I heard the man with the shofar go through the streets announcing that nobody was to talk to you. Your family is unclean. Your family is excommunicated. Your father—"

"Shut up! You mustn't talk to him!" hissed Nissim, hushing the child.

The boys walked off, and Ben-Zion stood dumbfounded. Suddenly he started to run. He ran out the gate and down to the office of *Hatzvi,* his father's newspaper. He seemed to see the large notice everywhere—on the walls of the city, on the fences of the houses, on the shutters of the shops. And the name Ben-Yehudah stood out in large, black letters. Why? What happened? Soon he would reach his father, and then the mystery would be solved. His father would explain it all to him. This must be a mistake—a terrible mistake. His father could never have done anything so evil. When he got to his father's printing shop, he went down the shabby stone steps to the cellar, where his father worked.

"Abba! Abba! What do they want from you? What are they after? What have you done to them?" Ben-Zion was shouting before he reached his father.

"Ben-Zion! What are you doing here? Why aren't you in school?"

"Nobody will have anything to do with me. They say that they mustn't talk to us. They lit black candles. What have we done to them, Abba? Why did they put up these large notices? What is it?" he asked, as the tears flowed down his cheeks.

"You are so excited, child," said Eliezer, placing his arm around his son's shoulder. "Come with me and I'll take you back to school. Don't pay any attention to these things. We must be very strong to be able to withstand them—you and I, together," He removed his dark coat, wiped his hands, took his son by his hand, and led him outside. Bilam, Eliezer's white donkey, stood outside.

"Come here, Ben-Zion, and climb on the donkey. I am going to take you back to school. Nobody will dare do anything to you. I promise you."

Ben-Zion sat behind his father on the donkey, hugging his thin back. Suddenly all his fears were gone. He felt safe. His father was going to take him back to school. He would explain everything to the children and the teachers. Nobody could harm him as long as he had his father at his side.

"Are you going to stay with me for a while?" he asked.

"Yes, Ben-Zion, take it easy."

The donkey broke into a trot. Ben-Zion began to cheer up. But when they passed the gray wall, he once more saw the large, accusing notices.

"What does it say, Abba?" he asked.

Eliezer halted the donkey and translated the contents to his son. "THE HATZVI IS HEREBY BANNED! NO RELIGIOUS JEW IS ALLOWED TO READ OR BUY THIS NEWSPAPER."

"But why, Abba?" Ben-Zion could not understand.

"Come, son, let us have a drink," said Eliezer. "I shall try to explain it to you, though I guess you are too young to understand what it is all about."

They got off the donkey near a large red gate, close to the gate of the Old City, and sat on tiny stools. Ben-Zion drank the cold drink made of date honey and crushed ice, and looked up at his father.

"You probably know that we Jews have a law called the Law of the Fallow Land. For six years we may plant the soil, but during the seventh it must be left to stand fallow. Nobody cultivates his fields, sows, or plants. This year is such a year, a fallow year. Only this time we may not keep it. The Jewish pioneers have only recently settled on the land and established the first Jewish settlements and planted fresh crops. If they were to stop their work for a year, they would lose all they have invested and borrowed, and Jewish agriculture would fail. So I wrote about this fallow year in my paper. And this is why the religious circles are so furious with me."

"Here he is! Here is the infidel! Beat him! Break his bones!" Loud voices came from the street corner. They saw a group of boys with earlocks down to their shoulders and dressed in long black coats, walking swiftly toward them from the end of the street. They approached Ben-Yehudah and his son, shouting wildly, "Here they are! Here they are!"

"Let's go home, Ben-Zion." Ben-Yehudah rose from his seat. They quickly got on the donkey—Ben-Zion in front and his father behind. The boys followed the donkey, running after it, beating it with long sticks, and screaming at the top of their voices, "A donkey's burial. That's what we'll give them. Bury them with their donkey." Soon they were joined by many adults who started stoning them and their donkey. Ben-Zion was very frightened and began to weep. "Abba! They will kill us!"

Ben-Yehudah urged the donkey on with all his strength, and the poor animal, who was being beaten on every side, galloped straight home—it knew the way well. Ben-Yehudah let the donkey gallop homeward and did not hold the reins. His arms clasped the boy, trying to protect him from the shower of rocks and sticks. "We shall be there in a minute or two," he said. When they reached the house he was about to dismount and open the gate, when it opened suddenly and the donkey trotted inside. Then the gate was shut behind them. Dvorah stood there with her back to the gate, after locking it with some difficulty. Her lips were trembling.

"Are you all right?" She could barely speak.

"Yes. We managed to get away in one piece. What are you doing here at this time of the day?" Eliezer seemed genuinely surprised.

"I was discharged from school," she told him, as she lowered her eyes.

"Do you mean to say that they discharged you because of my article?" His face blanched in fury.

"I suppose that that is the real reason. The headmistress told me that I had to leave on account of my cough, for health reasons. She said that as I was going to leave soon because of the baby, I had better take a year's vacation. They will contact me about teaching next year."

"Imma!" cried Ben-Zion. "How wonderful! You are going to have another baby? We must have a girl now, so that Yemima will have a sister!"

"There is plenty of time. The baby isn't due for months yet." Dvorah smiled at her son and then turned to face Eliezer. "And I was just beginning to think that we had reached a period of peace and quiet. We have just started paying back all our debts, buying all the things we need, and now . . . Soon we will have another mouth to feed, and here I am, out of a job. What will happen to your paper now? What shall we do, Eliezer?"

"We shall fight back," replied Ben-Yehudah. "That's what we are going to do!"

They could hear the shouting going on outside
their wall. Stones were thrown at the wall and the
gate. "Infidels! Blasphemers! You are excommunicated. Get out of Jerusalem while you can!"

"This will be a very difficult battle," whispered
Dvorah, her eyes brimming with tears. "A very difficult battle." She took Ben-Zion by his hand and led
him to the house.

"Tell me," asked Avichayil, "what is all that noise
out in the street? Why are they shouting like that?
Imma says that perhaps we won't go to school tomorrow. Don't you think that's great, Ben-Zion?"

Ben-Zion paid no attention to his brother. He was
thinking about the noise outside. How could they
fight everybody? Would the boys ever begin to talk to
him again? And what was all this strange business of
the Law of the Fallow Land? Why? What for? Everything was so strange and frightening.

## * thirteen

The ban against the Ben-Yehudah family continued.
The house seemed like a fortress under siege—nobody could enter or leave. Now and then people would
gather at the gate, hurl screams and abuse at the
Ben-Yehudah family and, occasionally, throw stones.

On the first day of the ban Ben-Yehudah tried to
send his sons to school.

"Don't," begged Dvorah. "Please don't. They will hit the children."

"Nobody is going to harm the children. They are not involved with my paper. They should go to school."

Ben-Zion and Avichayil left the gate, holding hands. Ben-Zion, who vividly remembered the events of the previous day, was trembling. But Avichayil was only waiting to fight. "Just let them try something! I will tear them to shreds!"

They did not get very far before they were surrounded by a furious mob.

"Here they are! Here are the sons of Yudke the infidel, the desecrators of the holy tongue!"

The children stood still, bewildered.

"Let us through or we'll be late for school," Ben-Zion tried saying pleasantly.

"We're not going to let them pass," shouted a voice in the crowd. Somebody threw the first stone. It hit Avichayil's arm, and he began to cry.

"Imma! Abba!" Ben-Zion started screaming at the top of his voice.

"Your Abba is busy. He is not going to come! He is busy writing another one of his filthy articles!" the voices mocked them. Large hands began to hit them.

"Run, Avichayil, run!" shouted Ben-Zion. But they were surrounded.

Help came suddenly. Solomon, the big, burly carpenter, made his way through the crowd.

"Shame on you!" he shouted furiously. "Beating helpless children, are you now? What on earth have the children done? Stop it immediately or I am going to break your necks." He raised his ax high over his head, as he stood towering over the children. Then he took the frightened boys home. The crowd let them pass and nobody attempted to hit them again. But they were followed by derisive whispers until they reached their house.

"Ben-Yehudah," said the big man as he faced Eliezer. "I am not a learned man. I have no idea whether you or the others are right. But do not let these lambs be involved in your affairs. They are children, Ben-Yehudah!" Then he turned and walked out of the yard.

"Oh, my darlings." Dvorah hugged her sons. "What have they done to you?" She wiped the blood from Avichayil's hand.

The children did not attempt to go to school after this incident. They stayed indoors, locked in the besieged house.

On the third day of the siege, Ben-Zion was roaming around the house with nothing to do. Avichayil was playing with little Yemima, and Eliezer stood at his desk working on his dictionary. Suddenly Ben-Zion noticed that his mother was sitting in a corner, writhing and biting her lips.

"Imma!" he cried. "What is it? What's wrong? Are you sick?"

"Yes child. . . . I think . . . I . . . am . . . in labor. . . . Ohh!" she groaned.

"But you said it was months away."

"It must be an early birth because of the excitement. . . . Ohh!" she groaned once more.

"Abba!" Ben-Zion rushed to his father. "Imma is in pain. She is about to give birth. What are we going to do?"

"Has the time come?" asked Eliezer, stroking Dvorah's head tenderly.

"Go and fetch Bracha, the midwife," murmured Dvorah.

Eliezer put his jacket on and left the house. Ben-Zion sat at his mother's side, her fingers gripping his small hands.

"Would you like a drink, Imma? Is there any way I can help you?"

"No, my pet, thank you. I will go and lie down on my bed. You look after the children." She rose heavily and walked to the other room.

Ben-Zion remained seated. He could hear his mother moaning and could hear her cries of pain. The minutes seemed to crawl like hours. Why wasn't his father back? When was Bracha going to come?

Avichayil went over to him. "Imma is crying. What's the matter, is she sick?"

"She is going to have a baby. Hush, Avichayil. Hush, Yemima. Sit here beside me." The three children huddled together, listening fearfully to their mother's groans from the next room.

It seemed as if ages passed before Eliezer returned, looking pale and soaked in perspiration. "They did not let me pass. They surrounded me and blocked my way. They said I was desecrating the Holy City. I tried to explain where I was going. I tried to tell them that a life was at stake, but they never listened. They paid no attention!"

"Eliezer, hurry! Call Salima, our Arab neighbor!" groaned Dvorah as she writhed on her bed.

"Salima? That toothless old hag?" Ben-Zion was upset. "How can she help Imma?"

"She speaks no Hebrew," said Eliezer. "I wouldn't like to have her . . ."

"Hurry, Eliezer, hurry!" shrieked the poor woman in desperation.

"But—" hesitated Eliezer.

"Hurry, Abba!" Ben-Zion cried. "Hurry! I will stay here with Imma."

Eliezer ran to the courtyard. Soon the bent, old, haglike Arab neighbor stood in the doorway. She signaled to them to leave the room, placed a copper basin on the fireplace, and lit the stove.

All night long the children heard their mother's terrible cries. It did not sound like their mother's voice at all; it sounded more like the cries of a hurt animal, fighting for its life.

The baby, the fourth Ben-Yehudah child, was born at dawn. Ben-Zion looked at her. She was a tiny creature without any hair. Her face was bluish and wrinkled.

"She is so tiny," whispered Dvorah weakly. "She can't even cry. Who knows whether she will remain alive?"

"What shall we call her?" asked Eliezer as he stroked his wife's hand.

"Shlomit—peace. Let us hope she brings us peace and quiet," whispered Dvorah.

"Peace?" Eliezer jumped from his chair. "Not peace. War!"

"Oh, Eliezer. I wish we had had some peace already. I am so tired of all this fighting. We shall name our daughter Shlomit," she said with a tone of finality.

"As you wish, my dear. Our daughter will be called Shlomit."

The tiny baby fought for her life. She gasped for air with her mouth wide open. Her ribs moved slowly and heavily under her dry skin.

"We must fetch a doctor, Eliezer. Something has to be done for the baby, and I am so weak," said Dvorah as she closed her eyes.

"Yes, we should really get a doctor," agreed Eliezer. He put his coat on. But how was he going to bring a doctor? They would not let him pass. They would block the way, stone him. "I am worried, Dvorah," he said. "Who knows whether—"

"I know!" Ben-Zion suddenly jumped up. "I am going to run over to Mount Scopus, to the monastery. One of the monks is a doctor. He knows me and he likes me. I will run very quickly and bring the doctor."

Before anybody had a chance to stop him, he raced from the house. He ran out of the city and climbed along the mountain path leading to the monastery of the Dominican friars. When he reached the gray building, he explained in broken syllables and sign language. The tall man in the white habit quickly returned downhill with him.

"Thank you," murmured Dvorah when she saw the monk at her bedside. She was coughing badly, and drops of blood appeared on her lips.

The monk stayed in the room a long time. His face looked very grim. He spoke to Eliezer in French. When the monk left, Ben-Zion ran over to his father. "What did he say, Abba?"

"He asks me why I do not come to the monastery to work on my dictionary. They, the non-Jews, understand me better than my own people."

"What did he say about Imma and the baby?" Ben-Zion asked impatiently.

"The baby is very weak. She must be wrapped in blankets. He cannot say whether she will live or die."

"And Imma? What of Imma?" His mother's fate was infinitely more important to him than the fate of the tiny, ugly creature who had caused his mother so much pain.

"Your mother is a very sick woman. The doctor says that she has to remain in bed for a long time. She caught consumption from me. Things never turn out the way we expect them to in this world. Years ago, doctors predicted that I had only one year to live, and here am I, alive and working. And your mother has caught the sickness from me, and now she is very weak."

"Do you mean to say Imma could actually die?" Ben-Zion was shocked.

"She is very sick. The doctor says that we must leave Jerusalem during the winter months. Your mother must be in a milder climate in order to grow stronger." Eliezer was talking to his son as if he were speaking to an adult. "We shall have to leave Jerusalem very soon. We shall go to Jaffa."

"Abba! Do your hear that noise? What is it?" Avichayil broke into the room.

Eliezer listened. Horses' hooves could be heard, and loud voices shouting, arguing.

"Ben-Zion, run outside and bar the gate!" Eliezer ordered his son. "Avichayil, shut all the windows."

"What is it, Abba?" asked the frightened Ben-Zion.

"Who knows what fresh trouble is about to befall us?"

The voices came closer. The horses' hooves clanged on the cobbled stones of the pavement.

"Abba, Abba, they are carrying a flag in their hands. I can see what is on it: THE FLAG OF THE CAMP OF JUDAH OF THE ARMY OF ISRAEL. I think these people are not our enemies, Abba!"

Ben-Yehudah rushed to the yard and peered through the iron bars. A very strange-looking crowd had gathered: a company of young men on horseback, dressed like Arabs, shouting very loudly, "Ben-Yehudah, our master and teacher. We have come to protect you!"

Surprised and excited, Ben-Yehudah opened the gate. "Who are you? Where do you come from?" he inquired.

"We are farmers and pioneers," they replied. "We come from Rishon-le-Zion, Hadera, Gedera, Zichron-Yaakov, Rosh Pinah, Mishmar Hayarden."

"We are the Shimshonim!" they announced.

"We heard of the ban and came to help you!"

The news of the arrival of the farmers and pioneers spread through Jerusalem like wildfire. Everybody spoke of the riders who came to protect Ben-Yehudah and his ideas. The battle was no longer waged between the many and the few, and the ban was broken and lifted. People began visiting the Ben-Yehudah family; they began to concern themselves with Dvorah's condition and with the new baby. Food poured into the house.

They would come into Dvorah's chamber, their eyes downcast.

"If this baby should die," murmured Chaya-Leah, the tea-vendor, "I shall never forgive myself."

"We are guilty. We have sinned against you," people said. "We listened to the nonsense and the hate-filled inciters. Can you forgive us?"

Suddenly the family was enveloped in warmth, devotion, and affection. They were no longer alone. The tiny baby began to get stronger. Women were watching over her day and night as if she was a precious jewel, keeping her warm and feeding her milk.

"She is going to live," announced the doctor. "But I am worried about Dvorah. You must leave Jerusalem immediately. The climate here is endangering her life."

## * fourteen

It was weeks before Dvorah was allowed to get out of bed. As soon as the doctor announced that they would be able to leave shortly, Eliezer began making arrangements. Friends and neighbors helped him pack. Eliezer left the editing of the paper to one of his trusted friends, who promised to publish it regularly and not to alter its policy. A horse and carriage were hired—in those days it was the only way people could travel long distances inland—and the family was ready to start its journey to Jaffa, where they were going to spend the cold winter months.

The children climbed happily into the carriage. Dvorah had a special seat arranged for her, so that she could recline with the baby in her arms. Eliezer held little Yemima. Avichayil and Ben-Zion sat in front, next to the coachman. This was their first long trip, and they were very excited. Soon the carriage left the winding lanes of Jerusalem. They went past dry, rocky mountains and Arab villages smelling strongly of smoke and manure. It was a lovely journey. Everything seemed strange and wonderful. The children could not get enough of the scenery and discussed their impressions in excited tones. When the carriage went quickly down a mountain slope, they were scared, and when their father left the carriage to help the driver push it uphill, they, too, went out to help.

It was dark by the time they left the mountains and reached the plain. The carriage made its way in the dark. Suddenly a full moon rose in the east, casting its pale light on everything. The moon rose slowly into a cloud-flecked sky, and in the distance they could hear the jackals making a sound like howling, lamenting women. Along the far-off horizon a camel caravan moved slowly toward them. In the moonlight the caravan seemed like a long necklace of triangles, with a small human form heading it. The sad tune of a flute seemed to accompany the crying jackals.

"Why is everything so beautiful and sad?" whispered Ben-Zion to the coachman.

"Go to sleep, child," replied the coachman. At that moment, his mind was not on Ben-Zion. He was wary of the caravan, which was drawing closer. The caravan halted, and the camels were ordered to get down to their knees on the narrow path; when the carriage reached it, it could not pass. The coachman expected the Arabs to remove the camels, but they settled down to their night's rest, lit a fire, sipped black coffee from their tiny cups, and showed no signs of getting up. In the meantime, a caravan of donkeys arrived from another direction. These were farmers, who began shouting at the camel drivers. The latter did not hold their tongues. The night had lost its stillness, and the sound of shouting and curses filled the air.

"What are we going to do?" wondered the coachman. "There is going to be a fight here, and we are right in the middle of it."

Avichayil, Yemima, and Shlomit slept in the carriage, without any care or concern. Ben-Zion, his father, and the coachman, however, were afraid. The coachman, who was well acquainted with the road customs of the East, had good reason to be worried, for the argument soon took another form and turned into a free-for-all. Sticks were raised, and the braying of the beaten donkeys mingled with human cries and the groans of violent, kicking camels. The carriage stood in the center of the battlefield, and the horses began neighing and rearing out of control. It was impossible to move in any direction.

Help came in the form of a closed carriage which arrived from the direction of Rishon-le-Zion. When the burly driver found himself in the whirlpool, he did not lose his wits. He quickly jumped off the carriage, and in the manner of the Arabs around him, began cursing loudly as he made his way through the excited human mass. He talked, explained, cajoled, and soothed. Soon tempers calmed down and voices grew softer. The Arabs ordered their camels up with a strange gurgling sound, and the carriage continued on its journey.

Ben-Zion was very tired. He had stayed up all night, and when he finally made up his mind to get inside the carriage and go to sleep, he noticed three horsemen riding toward them.

"What now?" Dvorah seemed very anxious.

"Imma, they have guns in their hands. They are pointing them at us." Ben-Zion was suddenly wide awake.

"Why do they want to kill us?" asked Avichayil, who had awakened from his sleep.

"What shall we do, Eliezer?" asked Dvorah, trembling. "We are lost."

"Faster," shouted Eliezer to the driver, who beat his horses mercilessly with his whip. But the tired horses moved wearily, and soon the horsemen reached them, their kefiyahs blowing in the wind, their knives on their hips. With one hand they held the reins of their horses, and with the other they held their guns. Cartridge belts were slung on their chests. Despite his fear, Ben-Zion found them attractive and could not stop admiring them.

"Abba," he suddenly called out. "I think it's Lolik! Oh, yes, it's Lolik!"

"Peace be upon thee!" the bewhiskered rider greeted them, setting the minds of the petrified passengers at ease with his smile.

"Lolik, how are you?" groaned Ben-Yehudah with a sigh of relief when he realized that the "Arab" was Lolik of Hadera, the scourge of the Arabs of the

Sharon Plain. It was the very same Lolik who only a few weeks before had headed the group that came to help the excommunicated family in Jerusalem. The other two "Arabs" were also Jewish guards from the Jewish settlements.

"What are you doing here?" Dvorah smiled in relief. "You gave us the fright of our lives."

"We heard that you were on your way to Jaffa, and we came to accompany you," explained Lolik.

The carriage, which was now accompanied by three guards, continued its journey.

Ben-Zion could not sleep. He watched the sturdy horsemen with admiration and excitement. "Imma," Ben-Zion begged, "I want to ride with Lolik on his horse." When Lolik's group had been in Jerusalem, he sometimes let Ben-Zion climb on his horse and then he would lead the horse around the city. All his friends were jealous when they saw him. But here, out in the open, Lolik could even make his horse gallop. This time they would go out for a real ride.

"Please, Lolik, can I?" he asked.

"It's fine with me, Ben-Zion, if your mother has no objections. What do you say, Mrs. Ben-Yehudah, can I take the boy for a ride? I will make a proper horseman out of him yet."

Dvorah agreed unwillingly, and soon the lucky boy was riding away with Lolik.

"I want to gallop, Lolik. Make him go faster," he called.

Lolik whispered something to his horse, pulled his bit, and the horse broke into a gallop. A cool wind blew through Ben-Zion's hair and disheveled it. He was held firmly by the strong man who sat behind him. "Scared, Ben-Zion?" smiled Lolik, as his whiskers tickled the boy's neck.

"No! Let's go faster!" called Ben-Zion with delight. Just then, the whole world was his.

The horse galloped over fields, through orchards and vineyards. Ben-Zion breathed in the fresh air, swallowed the green scenery. He was very happy.

"Oh!" He seemed quite shocked. "What's that over there?" An enormous expanse of blue, glimmering in the sunlight, was spread before them.

"That is the sea, Ben-Zion. Our Mediterranean. We shall soon reach Jaffa."

"The sea? It's lovely. I have never seen the sea before. It seems so big," said Ben-Zion, never taking his eyes off the shimmering vision ahead.

## * *fifteen*

Ben-Zion fell in love with the sea. This love grew stronger from day to day. Ben-Zion liked the place they lived in, for he could see the wide expanse of the water from every window.

The family was happy in Jaffa. In Jerusalem most of the population was made up of very traditional Jews, but most of the Jewish inhabitants of Jaffa were new immigrants. In Jaffa lived the pioneers, who had recently arrived in the country. They were a young, happy crowd of men and women who loved parties and singing. They welcomed the Ben-Yehudah family warmly and affectionately. They listened to Eliezer's opinions and innovations with enthusiasm. They were particularly enthusiastic over his attempts to revive the Hebrew language.

The mild climate was very good for Dvorah. Color came back to her cheeks and luster returned to her faded eyes. The baby, Shlomit, developed nicely. Eliezer was busy once more with his dictionary.

Ben-Zion was particularly happy in Jaffa. He clung to his friend Lolik and followed him wherever he went. The boy no longer needed anybody else. He did not miss the company of his own age group, nor did he need his parents. Now that he had Lolik and the wide blue sea, he had everything he could wish for.

Ben-Zion would take long walks along the seashore with Lolik and watch the wonderful sights with large, inquisitive eyes. Everything seemed so different, everything was new and exciting: the waves as they approached the white beach and seemed to swallow everything, and then suddenly, as if instructed by somebody, would retreat and leave the beach wet and glistening; the sea, which extended to the horizon; the ships, with their tall masts and oversized prows; windows which stared like round eyes; the stormy water, with waves and breakers. He loved to see the water suddenly grow calm, seeming to smile apologetically for its fury, and leave many gifts on the shore, seeming to placate him, make friends with him again. Ben-Zion collected these gifts of the sea: broken dishes and lovely shells.

For hours he would sit on a jutting rock which

overlooked the sea, making up wonderful dreams about the future. He would be a brave seaman sailing his boat to strange and distant lands across the horizon.

Ben-Zion became acquainted with some Arab sailors, one of whom was Abu-Hamis, Jaffa's most famous seaman. Abu-Hamis was a hefty man with a face tanned by the sun and the sea winds. His gait was rollicking, and Ben-Zion seemed like a dwarf beside him. Abu-Hamis told the most wonderful tales: stories of terrible storms, of distant lands and hidden rocks, of sunken boats at the bottom of the sea, and of man's constant battle against nature.

"Ben-Zion, where have you been all day? You are so dirty," Dvorah would scold him when he came home in the evening, filthy and hungry. "And when are we going to study, my boy?" she would ask.

Dvorah wanted to teach her children everything they were missing while they were away from school. But Ben-Zion's mind was not on his studies. He was drunk with the beach and the sea. He was only interested in hearing stories about the sea. So his mother told him of the ancient tribe of Dan, which lived on the seashore. His father drew a map of the tribes, painting the site of each tribe in a different color. "Paint the tribe of Dan in red—it's the prettiest color there is," begged Ben-Zion.

"Now I shall tell you about the days of the Judges," said Dvorah, but Ben-Zion's mind was elsewhere, outside. "Later, Imma. I must go down to the sea for a moment. It is so nice outside. You can tell me about this period tomorrow, can't you, Imma?" And without waiting for an answer, he dashed outside and ran down the winding lanes which led to the sea. There, near the rocks, he saw the many boats of the Arab boatmen and looked for Abu-Hamis's boat. Suddenly he noticed a boat which he had never seen before, a new boat painted in bright colors, and on its prow, in large Hebrew letters, he read CAPTAIN LOLIK. Lolik with a boat? Lolik a captain? He must take me sailing in his boat, thought Ben-Zion.

He ran down the rocky slope. "Where are you, Lolik?" he shouted. "Lo-lik!"

"Is it you, Ben-Zion?" boomed a voice from the boat, and Lolik emerged, standing up to his full height.

"Yes, it's me. You haven't been here all week long. I looked for you everywhere. Are you going to take me in your boat, Lolik?"

"What are you parents going to say?" hesitated Lolik.

"Abba is not even going to know, he is so busy with his dictionary, and Imma ... well ... she agrees," lied Ben-Zion as he lowered his eyes.

"Fine, my young seaman. Jump in. Come on, give me your hand. That's right. You are not afraid, are you now?" he smiled at Ben-Zion, who was standing in the boat like a veteran seaman, with legs spread apart.

"I have sailed with Abu-Hamis in his boat. But today I feel like going far away. OK, Lolik?" Ben-Zion's eyes entreated and demanded, and Lolik could not refuse.

"Fine, sailor boy. Anchors aweigh, my lad. We are off to the sea."

The anchor was raised, and the boat made its way

*Ehud (right), Ada (left), and Dola Ben-Yehudah, Ben-Zion's brother and sisters by his father's second wife, Chemdah, with their nurse*

*Eliezer Ben-Yehudah at work on the seventeen-volume* Thesaurus of the Hebrew Language *in his study in Jerusalem*

to the open sea. A small black cloud could be seen far away on the horizon.

"We are not going out very far, Ben-Zion. There is a storm brewing," said Lolik, watching the cloud anxiously. The boat went up and down the waves, sailing jauntily to the west. Ben-Zion stood at the helm, looking excitedly at the white-crested waves and the darkening skies.

"Let's return, Ben-Zion," said Lolik, turning the wheel. Suddenly a strong gust of wind came from the north. Great waves rose and broke on the beach. The sky was covered with clouds, and big drops of rain began to fall. The Arab sailors on the beach called to each other and brought their boats to safety near the large rock. Lolik, who was standing at the helm, was also about to return, but a strong gust of wind struck the sail and turned the boat toward the dangerous breakers.

How exciting—we're in the midst of a storm, just like those storms Abu-Hamis is always talking about, thought Ben-Zion as he held fast to the mast, enjoying every minute.

But Lolik did not seem to be enjoying the situation at all. He looked very stern and grave. "Hold fast to the helm and make sure that the waves don't wash you off the deck," he cried to Ben-Zion.

His warning was just in time. The boat spun around and around, and a wave swept the deck, practically carrying off Ben-Zion, who was holding on to the wet and slippery helm with all his strength. The boat rocked. The sail blew in all directions. The mast creaked and groaned. "Watch out, Ben-Zion!" shouted Lolik. The mast suddenly snapped and fell near the helm with a loud thud. Ben-Zion jumped aside, but Lolik was injured. Ben-Zion gazed at the cut on Lo-lik's hand. Lolik was bleeding.

"Does it hurt, Lolik?" Ben-Zion hugged his friend. "What will happen now? Are we going to drown?"

"Don't worry, Ben-Zion. Everything will be fine." Lolik tried to calm Ben-Zion, but his face did not look reassuring.

"Are we going to die today, Lolik?" Ben-Zion asked anxiously, as he looked at the sea which was threatening to swallow the boat with its two sailors. Death seemed to be sending many arms toward him in the form of thundering waves breaking into mil-lions of drops in an earsplitting din.

Lolik was trying desperately to turn the boat southward, but the waves were too strong for him. A large wave washed across the deck. It was followed by another wave and another. Now they were in water up to their knees. They could hear the Arab sailors shouting to each other in the distance. But the beach seemed very far away.

"I will never sail again," wept Ben-Zion. He sat in the bottom of the boat, wet and shivering with cold and dread, his head spinning from the whirling boat.

"Don't cry, Ben-Zion. Look, look over there! Some-one is coming to help us. Come on, have a look, Ben-Zion!"

Ben-Zion raised his eyes. A large boat was head-ing in their direction.

"That's the boat of Abu-Hamis!" he cried happily. "I know it. He is coming to help us. I knew that he would never let us drown."

The gray boat came slowly, battling the stormy

waves. Ben-Zion clung to Lolik. Now they both stood in the water as the boat swayed and rose without helm or sail, at the mercy of the wind and the waves.

Time seemed to stand still until the boat reached them. A rope was thrown overboard, and a pair of strong arms grabbed him and placed him at the bottom of a dry boat. Abu-Hamis wrapped him up in his coat and covered him with a blanket made of goat's wool. Yet his teeth were chattering and he could not get warm.

The sound of the waves mingled with the voice of Abu-Hamis, who stood at the helm, intoning, "God, why do You have to drive me crazy—after all, I love You."

By the time the boat reached the shore, Ben-Zion had fainted. Lolik carried him in his strong arms like a sick baby and took him home.

All evening a doctor sat by the bedside of the feverish boy, listening carefully to his breathing and giving him medicines in small doses. At midnight he got up from his seat.

"I must go now, Mrs. Ben-Yehudah," he said. "Make sure the boy gets his medicines regularly and keep him covered. You must stay up to watch him tonight. I shall be back in the morning. If the crisis passes tonight, he will be out of danger."

Dvorah sat at her son's bedside all through the night, wiping the perspiration off his forehead with a damp cloth and giving him hot drinks. The boy was unconscious and spoke feverishly. At dawn Eliezer took her place, and Dvorah went into the next room to feed the baby. The baby was still in her arms when Eliezer's screams made her jump from the chair.

"Dvorah! Dvorah! Come here quickly!"

"What's happened?" she cried, running into the room. Ben-Zion's condition seemed no worse than before. He was lying on the bed as she had left him, moaning and muttering.

"Do you hear what he is saying, Dvorah? Can you hear him?" Eliezer's fists were clenched, and he was livid.

"He is feverish, Eliezer. Don't worry, he will be better soon," Dvorah tried to calm her husband.

"But listen to him, Dvorah. Just listen!"

Ben-Zion was repeating Abu-Hamis's words in Arabic: "God, why do You have to drive me crazy— after all, I love You."

"Can you hear him? He is angry at the god of the sea. He speaks Arabic! The first Hebrew child speaks Arabic when he is feverish! Dvorah, we have failed!" Eliezer covered his face with his thin hands and left the room, trembling.

"I love You—why do You drive me crazy?" Ben-Zion continued to mumble in Arabic.

## * sixteen

Ben-Zion felt better. He stopped mumbling, his forehead became cooler, and his breathing was relaxed and quiet. The crisis was over. In the morning Lolik came to visit him, still dressed in the clothes he had worn the day before. The clothes had dried and hardened and smelled strongly of salt and seaweed. Lolik was very pale, his face covered with black stubble. There was a bluish scar on his left cheek, running down from the corner of his eye to his mouth. His eyes were bloodshot. Lolik, the brave watchman, who was the scourge of the Arabs of the plain, was now worried and miserable. He blamed himself entirely for taking Ben-Zion out in the storm. Dvorah felt sorry for him and tried to calm him.

"After all, you could hardly be expected to know what was going to happen," she told him. "Stop blaming yourself. See, he is feeling better already. I am going to bring you a cup of tea."

Lolik stood by Ben-Zion's bedside. The boy slept peacefully. Lolik knelt beside him and whispered, "Forgive me, Ben-Zion, my friend."

Ben-Zion slowly opened his eyes, looked around, and asked, "Is it you, Uncle Lolik? Where am I? What happened?"

Gradually his memory returned, and he shuddered.

"It is all over now. You are home and healthy and all in one piece," said Dvorah, stroking his hair. "Go back to sleep, child." Ben-Zion shut his eyes and fell into a deep sleep. "You, too, had better go to sleep," she told Lolik. "Ben-Zion is out of danger." Lolik heaved a deep sigh of relief and left the house.

Dvorah entered Eliezer's room and informed him that their son was feeling much better.

"I am pleased to hear that his body is in a better state," said Eliezer, as he lifted his eyes from a pile of papers, "but what of his soul? What of his Hebrew?"

The fanatic light gleamed in Eliezer's eyes again. "It is his Hebrew which is diseased. Badly diseased. He spoke Arabic! The first Hebrew child is a disappointment, Dvorah. He has not fulfilled my anticipations."

"But he was speaking in his fever. He had no idea he was speaking Arabic," replied Dvorah, trying to defend her son.

"But that's just it! When he is conscious he speaks Hebrew. But subsconsciously, in his heart, he betrays the language. Hebrew has not really taken root in his soul. It was a mistake on my part to let him mingle with people who speak no Hebrew. They have proved to be the wrong company for him. He must be forbidden to meet them. We shall soon go back to Jerusalem, and he is going to stay home until Hebrew is so ingrained in him that nothing can shake it."

"Spare the child, Eliezer," begged Dvorah, with tears in her eyes. Was Ben-Zion doomed to stay home again?

The next morning Dvorah informed Ben-Zion that they were soon to go back to Jerusalem. Ben-Zion was furious.

"But what for, Imma? We're all so happy here. We came here to spend the winter, and only three weeks have passed since we arrived. Why do we have to return?"

"It is your father's will," she replied.

"He always gives orders and commands. We must always do the things he wants us to do. He is a tyrant, a real tyrant," Ben-Zion mumbled to himself. He knew that arguing with his mother was useless. In her eyes, his father's word was law. And to attempt to change his father's mind was absolutely hopeless. Abba would not give in.

"May I go down to the sea to bid it farewell and visit with my friends for the last time?" he asked with tears in his eyes.

"Go on, child. But don't stay too long. Your father has serious objections to your friendship with Arab children and sailors."

"Why?"

I must explain it to him, thought Dvorah. He must be made to understand. But could a seven-and-a-half-year-old boy understand his father's battle and struggle? While she was still deliberating, the boy left the house and went down to the sea.

It was noontime. The sea was calm and blue. White sails flitted across the horizon and gulls hovered over the water. Was this the very same sea which raged so violently only a few days before? The boy skipped along the beach, inhaling the scent of the sea —a smell of seaweed, salt, fish, and distant worlds. The sailors surrounded him and greeted him happily in a mixture of Arabic and broken Hebrew. "Here is our young sailor. The fellow who is not afraid of the sea!"

"Ben-Zion is brave!" Abu-Hamis praised him, slapping his shoulder. This praise from the lips of the great sailor was very sweet. Even the children greeted him with admiration. Everybody wanted to hear his exploits—which he told willingly.

" . . . and then, a great big wave came along and almost swept me off . . . ," he told them proudly. The children looked at him with awe.

'You're OK, Ben-Zion. You are a real tough guy. Tomorrow I am going to give you a really good time," said Abu-Hamis with a broad smile. "I shall take all the children in my boat to the distant rocks, and we are going to fish all day long. We are going to spend the whole day in the water. How's that for a celebration?"

"It's great! Terrific!" the children shouted happily.

"We shall light a fire and grill the fish," called out the freckled Chaim.

Everybody was very excited. Ben-Zion was the only one who did not seem delighted at the prospect.

"Don't you want to come? Afraid of the sea already?" Abu-Hamis could not understand the reason for the boy's sad expression.

"No. It's not that. I cannot come with you. We are returning to Jerusalem tomorrow."

"Returning? But you were going to spend the whole winter here in Jaffa. Why are you going back?" The children were at a loss to understand this, as were Abu-Hamis and the other Arab sailors.

"My father wants us to return," said Ben-Zion. He could think of no other reason.

"Your father is a bad man!" exclaimed Nissim.

"He is crazy. Even my father says so. He says that he is just plain crazy and that he will drive your whole family nuts with his craziness," said David seriously.

"My mother says that your mother is always sick only because of him. She looks so sick and old just because he causes her so much trouble with his crazy ideas about Hebrew and his newspaper. He is always picking fights with everybody, and you never have enough to eat in your house," said another boy.

"He is a wicked man!" the children agreed.

Ben-Zion agreed with them. The children only confirmed all his innermost feelings. Suddenly he jumped up and cried, "You know what? Let's go and declare war on him!"

"Come on, boys. Let's go!" they shouted. "Let's find some rotten fruit and vegetables in the market and declare war on him. Let him find out what you get if you are such a wicked man—and crazy to boot!"

The children liked the idea. They ran to the market and collected everything they could lay their hands on. They gathered sticks, filled their pockets with stones, and waited in ambush for Ben-Yehudah around a bend in the street. David climbed on a roof and stood guard to warn them of his arrival. He was going to get what was coming to him.

Ben-Yehudah walked slowly. He was dressed in his oriental clothes, a red tarbush on his head and horn-rimmed glasses on his nose. He was smoothing his pointed, reddish beard with one hand and carrying a bundle of books in the other. He was lost in reverie and did not notice what was going on around him.

"Get ready boys, he's coming!" the message flew. Suddenly a volley of rotten vegetables struck the bewildered Ben-Yehudah.

"Go on! Let him have some more. That crazy fellow. That wicked man!" shouted the children, throwing everything that came to hand. "Crazy, crazy! Tyrant! Cruel father!"

"What's going on here?" wondered people who had gathered around in the street to watch this strange sight.

"Oh! That's Ben-Yehudah the infidel," they told each other. "The children have opened a campaign against him. Even his own son has joined the fight!"

"Well, that's just what he deserves. He raised a stubborn and rebellious son. He had better not set a bad example for our own children!"

"Get out of Jaffa!"

"Nobody wants you here, Ben-Yehudah. Go back to Jerusalem!"

The adults, too, found that to be a good moment to strike at Ben-Yehudah. They had opposed him and his ideas all along, but were afraid of coming out in the open, for they dreaded his popularity among the pioneers. But now they found the opportunity to express their feelings.

Ben-Yehudah was furious and surprised. He wiped the dirt from his face and did not know what to do. A few minutes later he came to himself. He raised his head and walked stiffly home. Suddenly he noticed his son among the crowd. He grabbed him and dragged him home with him. Then he locked the door behind him, leaned on it for a minute while he breathed very heavily, and watched his son in silence. He could not understand why his son had been among his enemies and tormentors.

"Go on, beat me," cried Ben-Zion, staring his father in the face. "Beat me as much as you like. I don't care. You're a tyrant! Everybody says you're cruel to your children and everybody hates you!"

Ben-Zion was fully prepared to receive a thrashing from his father. But to his great surprise his father just stood there, dumbfounded. His eyes were full of sorrow. For a long time he stood and watched his son mournfully. Then he went to his room and slammed the door behind him.

"I shall run away from home. I shall sail in Lo-lik's boat!" Ben-Zion hurled his screams at the closed door.

# * *seventeen*

Dvorah heard Ben-Zion's shouts and ran into the room. "What is wrong, my child?" she asked, trembling. "Why are you speaking to your father like this? Do you want me to die of sorrow?"

Ben-Zion looked at his pale mother, who was trembling like someone afflicted with the ague. Yes, the others had been right. He could see clearly how his mother had aged. Her face was lined, and there were white streaks in her lovely dark hair. He was filled with pity for her. All the braveness against his father crumpled before his weeping mother.

"I do love you, Imma. I love you most in the whole world." He went over to her and hugged her. "It's only because of him that I want to run away. He only knows how to give orders. I have to do everything his way. He is even cruel to you. It is because of him that you are so weak and pale."

"Don't ever speak about your father like that," Dvorah told him quietly. "Your father loves us very much."

"People who love you don't act the way he does. You love me and I can feel your love. But I never feel his love for me."

"You are mistaken, my child. He loves you very much in his own way."

"Yes. I should have known. You're always on his side. But I can't stand his tyranny. I'm not a baby. I'll be eight soon. I want to be like other children. I want to be free, to play, to run about the streets, like David and Chaim. I want to be like everybody else. Why doesn't he let me, Imma?"

"You are right, Ben-Zion. You are no longer a baby. And that is why you must know more about your father and his struggle. If you know more about it, you may be able to understand him, forgive him. I will come to your bedroom after supper and talk to you."

This was the story Dvorah told her son that evening.

"Your father was born in the town of Lushki in Russia in the year 1858. His family, the Perelmanns, owned a small grocery store, from which they could barely scrape a living. When your father was a young child, his father died, leaving behind a young widow with five small children. Her wealthy brother agreed to raise Eliezer and see to his education. Even as a very small child he was considered brilliant, and his family hoped he would become a rabbi. So his uncle sent him to study in a yeshiva.

"The boy showed great promise. But he found Jewish and religious studies insufficient, for he was interested in everything. He would listen to people speaking in the street, he would read books and papers about science and literature and politics. His uncle did not approve of this kind of reading. Why should a boy who was studying to become a rabbi read secular literature? He was furious with Eliezer and warned him not to stray from what he considered to be the right path.

"One evening Eliezer was reading an abridged Hebrew translation of *Robinson Crusoe* in his bed. The book was spellbinding, and he read it by candlelight. Suddenly he heard a creak on the stairs. He recognized his uncle's footsteps. The uncle had forbidden him to read any literature, so he quickly put the candle out, hid the book under his mattress, and pretended to be asleep. His uncle opened the door quietly. He was suspicious. A moment ago he had seen a crack of light under the boy's door, but now it was dark and Eliezer was sleeping soundly. He touched the candle and felt the wick. It was still warm. He realized that the boy was deceiving him. In a tantrum, he began searching the room and soon discovered the book under Eliezer's mattress. 'You infidel, you!' he screamed. 'Here I am, feeding you, teaching you, clothing you, and you, you just go ahead and read these evil books! You are desecrating the holy tongue with these secular books. Get out of my house immediately!' And he lifted his hand to beat him.''

Dvorah paused for a moment and breathed heavily.

"Go on, Imma," whispered the wide-eyed boy, his eyes glued to her face.

"Well, child, your father left the house. It was night, and it was cold and snowing outside. Where could he go? 'Return to your mother,' shouted his uncle. 'And take this talith with you. You are going to need it for prayers and repentance. Tell your mother that I will have nothing to do with any of the Perelmanns again.' He threw the talith at the boy and shut the door of his house.

"Eliezer walked through the streets of the town. He was afraid to return to his mother's home. He was scared that she would be angry. Where could he go? The streets were dark, and snow was falling. He buttoned his coat up to his neck, stuck his hands in his pockets, and went out of town on the road leading to the neighboring town, Glovokyeh. Eventually he got there. He was very cold, and he did not know his way about, for he was a stranger in that town. He walked about, miserable and lonely, full of indignation at the great injustice that had been done him. After all, what was wrong with reading those books? Why shouldn't books like *Robinson Crusoe* be published in Hebrew? What could be wrong with that? He could not understand it."

"Neither do I, Imma."

"There were many people who regarded Hebrew as a holy language, a language intended for prayers and religious literature. They believed that any other use of the language constitutes sacrilege. Many people still think so today. Now, where were we? Oh yes, the boy, Eliezer, was walking through the strange town. It was midnight, everything was dark and still, there was nobody out in the streets. Eliezer headed for the synagogue, where he lay down on a wooden bench and fell asleep. When the men came to pray in the morning, they discovered a thin, pale boy, curled up in his overcoat, shivering with cold. My father, who was one of the early risers, took the boy home with him and adopted him. Eliezer became a brother to us—and to me he meant even more than a brother. From the moment I first saw him, I loved him with all my heart. Eliezer remained with my family for a number of years. He was able to study to his heart's content. He could expand his knowledge, and nobody interfered with his choice of reading material. On the contrary, he was always given the best books, on any subject he wanted. He learned languages and his horizons broadened. When he became a young man, he decided to go out into the world and complete his education. He wanted to be a doctor. I was heartbroken when he left, but I knew that he had to study and that I must do nothing to stop him.

"He sent us many letters, telling us about his studies, his meetings with interesting people, his new ideas. Then he became sick, very sick. He caught tuberculosis. He had to give up the study of medicine—the doctors believed he only had a very short time to live. But he did not despair. About that time, a number of freedom movements sprang up in various countries which were ruled by foreign nations. The movements demanded freedom and national independence, and fought for their ideas. Eliezer became convinced that the time had come to liberate the Jewish people from the yoke of the Diaspora. He favored the return to the land of Israel. The land was to be repopulated, and its people would fight for their right to have their own country once again. They would revive its deserts. But the first step was to speak a common language which could unite all the immigrants. Without a common language this difficult task could never be achieved."

"Yes, Imma, that's right. Remember the story of the people of Babel, who wanted to build a tower reaching the sky? God jumbled their language, and they were unable to work together. Do you remember the story?"

"Yes, darling, You are quite right. And the thing the Jews wanted to do in this country was far more complicated that the building of the Tower of Babel. They had to cross oceans, gather from all the corners of the world, fight for their right to the land of their fathers, fight the people who prevented them from building a homeland. Your father realized that without a language to unite all the Jews this could never be accomplished. Only one language was possible—the ancient Hebrew language, the language of the Jewish people. This would be the uniting force, the one thing which would help return the land to its people.

"So your father began working for his cause with all that was in him. He was a sick man. He thought his days were numbered. So he tried to find others who would support his idea. He published articles in Jewish newspapers explaining his ideas. He signed his articles with the pen name Ben-Yehudah—son of Judah—and later made that his real name.

"But writing and making speeches were not enough for him. He went into politics, studied the problems of Palestine, the history of its Arab population, its system of government—the Turkish government—and the condition of the Jews in the various countries of the Diaspora. He studied day and night, and one day he reached the conclusion that he had to immigrate to Palestine and practice the things he was writing and talking about. There were many people who tried to dissuade him. Palestine seemed a very backward country, far away in the East. People felt that an educated and cultured man like your father would be much better off in a country like France, where he could further his ambitions and voice his opinions. But Eliezer paid no attention to them. He said that if he really believed that this was the right way for Jews, then it was up to him to live here. He said that he wished to spend his few remaining years in the land of Israel. That was the answer he gave his friends who tried to change his mind."

"He was right, wasn't he, Imma?"

"Yes, dear, he was. But in those days most of the important Jewish leaders lived outside of the land of Israel. They thought your father's actions were very strange. But your father knew that he had to do what he thought was right. He came to our house and asked me whether I would be willing to join him. After our marriage we left home and came to the land of Israel.

"It was here that your father actually began to fulfill his ideas. He edited *Hatzvi,* where he published his views on the rehabilitation of the country, on agriculture, on his attitude to religion. He wrote articles which set the population of Jerusalem against him. This population lives on donations sent by Jews abroad. Your father maintains that Jews should return to the land and live like a normal nation, with farmers and craftsmen who do not exist on donations. Your father has many new and revolutionary ideas, the most important of which is the revival of the Hebrew language. And even here, just as in the small Russian town, there are many people who claim that the use of Hebrew in daily life is a terrible sin."

"But I don't understand, Imma. Didn't people speak Hebrew in the time of the Bible?" asked Ben-Zion.

"Yes, child, they did. But after the destruction of the Second Temple the Jews dispersed. They forgot their language. Hebrew was only to be found in the Holy Scriptures and prayer books, and people forgot that it had ever been a living language, like every other language in the world. But this opposition did not prevent your father from continuing his campaign. He started to work on a Hebrew dictionary, and now he spends as much as eighteen hours a day working on this project. For the past ten years he has been involved in the revival of the Hebrew language— from the day he first came to this country. This is his life's work, and he is prepared to give up everything he has for the realization of this dream. At times it appears that he is even ready to sacrifice our lives for his ideals. Hebrew is the most important thing in your father's life."

Dvorah paused for a moment, then continued quietly.

"I know that your father has hurt us. Our family is different from other families, your mother is different from other mothers, and you, his children, are different from other children. And the battle is not yet over. We shall have to suffer with your father until his ideals are realized. And we must help your father. I know that you suffer a great deal. But we have to learn to accept our fate with love.

"One day, Ben-Zion, everybody in this country will speak Hebrew. It will be taught in kindergartens and schools. Books will be written and published in Hebrew, and the sounds of our revived ancient language will be heard everywhere. And when that day comes, my son, we shall know just why we had to suffer. On that day everybody will recognize your father's great work. And people will appreciate our patience and suffering, the hardship and privation we underwent for the realization of this great dream."

"Imma, will that day ever come?" asked Ben-Zion with shining eyes.

"Yes, child. That day will surely come. I do not know when it will come, but I know it will. And when babies first prattle in Hebrew, everybody will remember you, my son, the first Hebrew child."

"Will it take a long time?"

"I hope you will see the day. Will you promise me always to obey your father and never to oppose his will?"

Suddenly the dream of the good times ahead vanished, and Ben-Zion returned to reality, where his father wanted to lock him indoors and not allow him to play in the street.

"But Imma . . ." objected the eight-year-old.

"I want you to promise, Ben-Zion—please," Dvorah interrupted his words. She was suddenly racked by a fit of coughing. Her forehead was covered in sweat, and her hands became cold and clammy.

"Imma, what is it? What's wrong?" Ben-Zion was very frightened.

"Promise me!" she whispered in a tired and

hoarse voice. "I don't know how much longer I will still be with you. Please, child, promise me that you will never oppose your father in his fight for the Hebrew language. Please, child. . . ."

"I promise," whispered Ben-Zion. To ease her suffering he would have promised her anything.

## * *eighteen*

Shortly after the family's return to Jerusalem, Dvorah became pregnant again. This time she was much sicker than before. She coughed and spat blood. Her body became extremely feeble, her eyes sank into their sockets, and her face looked thin and wan. She seemed to be fading away before the eyes of her friends. Her sickness, the terrible living conditions, the frequent births—all these were shortening her life.

Eliezer tried to cheer her up. Things seemed to be improving financially. Many of the new immigrants and pioneers backed Ben-Yehudah. He had many new subscribers, and there was more money. Eliezer's enemies were afraid of voicing their opinions in public. In the new settlements he found many followers among the pioneers, who began to insist on Hebrew in their homes. His dream of the revival of Hebrew was winning interest and support throughout the Jewish world. Work on the dictionary was progressing.

They should have been very happy. But Dvorah was no longer in a condition to enjoy anything. Most of the time she simply sat in her chair, moaning, coughing, and spitting blood. Whenever she got up and moved around, she would drag her feet and choke on her coughing. She had tuberculosis. Fifteen years before the doctors had predicted Eliezer's early death from this sickness; now it was Dvorah who was dying of the disease, while Eliezer seemed to have overcome it.

After she gave birth to their fifth child, a daughter, Dvorah could not rise from her bed. But when she saw the lovely little child, a weak smile lit up her face.

"We shall name her Atara—crown," said Eliezer, "the crowning glory of our life." And Dvorah agreed.

Dvorah stayed in bed for many weeks. The children were neglected, for there was nobody to look after them and feed them properly. Ben-Yehudah worked all day on his newspaper and dictionary, and the small children ran through the house like a pack of orphans. Dvorah would lie in her bed and watch her children, hungry and dirty. She tried to get up, but was too weak. After every attempt, she was attacked by a terrible fit of coughing.

In his misery Eliezer wrote to his old mother in Russia and asked her to come look after his children and the sick Dvorah. His mother agreed to come right away.

But a new problem cropped up. The Turkish officials did not allow Jews to immigrate to Palestine for fear of aggravating the situation between the Jews and the Arabs, and they refused to grant the old woman her entry visa to the country. Ben-Yehudah appealed to the pasha of Jerusalem, but with little success. Finally, friends suggested to Ben-Yehudah that he should try smuggling his mother into the country.

When old Feigaleh arrived at the port of Jaffa illegally, without a visa, Eliezer's friends packed her into a potato sack and smuggled her into the country with a load of potatoes. Two sailors, who had been bribed in advance, saw to it that the sack reached the hotel where Eliezer was waiting for his mother.

The old woman had not seen her son for many years. He was a young lad when he left, full of life and glowing ambitions. And here was a bent man, his face lined with bitterness and frustration. She hugged and kissed him and asked after his health. But Eliezer stood there, as cold as stone.

"In the land of Israel I speak only Hebrew," he told her. "I am terribly sorry, but if you wish to speak to me, you must learn Hebrew." Her tears were useless. Her son did not speak to her throughout the long journey from Jaffa to Jerusalem.

The old lady was shocked when she saw the condition of the family. Dvorah lay sick in bed, the children ran around, dirty, neglected, and hungry. Filth and misery peered out of every corner.

The good woman did the best she could. She washed the children, cooked their meals, and sewed new clothes for them. Ben-Yehudah had warned her not to address his children in Yiddish, and young Ben-Zion was determined to teach his seventy-year-old grandmother some Hebrew. This was no simple undertaking, and neither the pupil nor the teacher could see any real results. When Ben-Yehudah realized how difficult things were for his mother and children, he allowed her to address them in Russian, but not in Yiddish. He insisted on that. He would not tolerate Yiddish at any price!

Dvorah's condition became grave, and finally the doctor ordered that she be taken to the hospital. Now she was burdened by the additional agony of having to leave her children. She was given an isolated room on the top floor. The children were only allowed to visit her once a week, and then only from a distance, in order to prevent infection. Little Shlomit and the baby, Atara, who were too young to understand anything, were delighted to see their mother and held out their little plump arms toward her. Ben-Zion, Avichayil, and Yemima would stand and weep from a distance.

"Don't cry, my darlings," Dvorah would whisper tenderly. "I am soon going to get well, and then I shall return home."

Ben-Zion, the eldest child, was the only one who was permitted to sit next to his mother when the younger children left. Dvorah would then wrap her hands in a clean towel, and thus, without actually touching each other, they could hold hands. Whenever he came to see her, she would beg, "Ben-Zion, my child. You promised, remember!"

A few weeks later, Dvorah was well enough to leave the hospital and return home. This was a period of great happiness for the family. They had moved to a larger house with plenty of trees and a garden in the back. Dvorah would sit in the garden surrounded by her children, read stories, and listen to the way they shouted and played. The sun would warm her tired body. The green trees and chirping birds filled her heart with joy.

Ben-Zion spent many hours with his mother, as if his heart told him that he would soon lose her. He did not go out to play with his friends and ignored his books and studies.

"Do you see this tree, Ben-Zion?" she asked one day, pointing at the palm tree which stood at the back of the garden. "When you were first born we wanted to call you Itamar—an island of palms—for I love this tree. Just see how proud and tall it stands."

"I like that name. Itamar. It sounds much nicer than Ben-Zion. Why did you call me Ben-Zion, Imma?"

"There were many people who objected to such a name. They said it was not a suitable name for a Jewish child. A Jewish boy should be called Avraham, Yitzhak, Moshe, or David, or some other biblical name. Why Itamar? Your father gave in on that occasion and called you Ben-Zion."

"I prefer Itamar. One day when I am grown up, I shall change my name to Itamar."

Days flowed by, calmly and quietly. Ben-Zion was nine years old now, a very good and handsome boy. Avichayil was sturdy, active, and tough. Three-year-old Yemima was a lively little girl, who, to her parents' great delight, spoke very fluent Hebrew. They loved listening to her bell-like voice singing and chattering all day. Little Shlomit had developed nicely and was now reaching the age when she was beginning to make up small sentences. The baby, Atara, was the prettiest of their daughters, the crown and glory of her adoring family.

One night Ben-Zion woke up to the sound of footsteps and excited voices. What has happened to Imma? he wondered, running barefoot to her bed. His grandmother, Feigaleh, stood next to his mother's bed, holding Dvorah's hands. His mother was finding it very difficult to breathe.

"Dvorah, my love, what is it, sweetheart?" asked Eliezer, kneeling at the bedside.

"This . . . is . . . the end. . . . I . . ." murmured Dvorah. "Eliezer . . . promise to . . . bring over . . . my sister Pola. . . . She will make you . . . a good wife . . . and be a good . . . mother . . . to . . . my children. . . . Eliezer . . ."

"Stop it, darling. Don't talk this way. You are going to get better."

"No. This . . . is . . . the end. . . . Swear . . . Eliezer . . . swear . . ."

"I swear," said Eliezer. Looking at his mother, he said quietly, "I am going for a doctor," and dashed out the door.

"Imma, Imma," cried Ben-Zion.

"My child . . ." mumbled Dvorah. "Your promise . . . Remember your promise. . . . Never forget your promise . . . about your father. . . . He loves you. . . . Be good. . . . Help him. . . . Promise. . . ." She said no more.

When the doctor arrived, he looked at her wordlessly and then covered her face with a sheet. "She is no longer with us," he said quietly.

Eliezer stood with his head bent low, his hand on Ben-Zion's shoulders, and murmured, "Your mother is dead. She is no longer with us. She has departed from us." He was weeping as he patted his son's head. "Try and be strong, child. Nothing will ever bring our mother back to us."

Ben-Zion was shocked. He looked at his mother's covered body and could not grasp what had happened. But she is here! He could see her! How was it possible that she was no longer there with them? He walked across the room to the bed, intending to hug his mother, remove the sheet which covered her face, and show everybody that she was still there. But his father moved him tenderly away from the bed.

"You no longer have a mother, my child," he said.

"But she is here. I can see her! Let me go over and hug her. Imma, please don't leave me. You are the only one I have. Imma, don't go away from me!" His mother lay without moving under the white sheet.

Avichayil and Yemima woke up to the sounds of his screaming. They stood at the doorway. Avichayil could not understand what was happening. "Imma is gone? Where to?" he muttered sleepily, and returned to bed.

Yemima also could not understand what had happened. Ben-Zion was the only child who realized that he would never see his mother again.

The next morning they accompanied Dvorah on her journey. Three people followed the coffin, which was borne by the members of the burial society. Three lonely mourners: Eliezer, his son Ben-Zion, and the loyal family friend, Nissim Bechar. Old Feigaleh stayed at home with the little ones.

None of the citizens of Jerusalem came to pay their final respects to Dvorah. The rabbis had proclaimed her unclean and had excommunicated her.

"Ben-Yehudah's wife will not be buried inside a Jewish cemetery," they announced. Their proclamation frightened the citizens of the city. "We have not lifted the ban from the Ben-Yehudah family. He is an infidel, and anybody who has anything to do with him or his family will be excommunicated!" These were the words of the rabbis at the time of mourning. It was only when Ben-Yehudah threatened to disclose the scandal to the world that the burial society consented to bury the body within the cemetery and not behind the fence, as they had first intended.

The three stood silently on the Mount of Olives at the foot of the freshly dug grave. Blue skies stretched overhead. All around them the peace and silence of a summer noon were evident.

"Come, child. We shall go back home. Everything is over now," whispered Eliezer, putting his arms around his son's shoulders.

But Ben-Zion refused to budge from the grave. "Imma, my Imma," he wept bitterly. "Now I have nobody left in the world. Why did you leave me, Imma?"

## * nineteen

Neglect was evident in every corner of the Ben-Yehudah household. "Imma, Imma," mumbled Atara and Shlomit. "Where is Imma?" asked Yemima and

Avichayil. "Why doesn't she come back to us? Why can't we go and visit her?"

Only Ben-Zion understood that their mother was gone and would never come back again.

When the younger children would pester their grandmother and ask her when their mother would return, the old woman would reply, "One day." They waited anxiously for this "one day" to materialize. When they opened their eyes in the mornings they would ask, "Grandma, is today the 'one day' you told us about? Will Imma return today?"

The old woman was unable to answer these questions. Her daughter-in-law's death had broken her physically. She walked around like a ghost, her eyes watering, her lips murmuring prayers.

It was impossible to speak to their father, for he was busy with his own affairs and had locked himself in his private world even more than before. He did not talk to the children for days on end, and when they addressed him, he did not answer. He spent most of his time outside the house, working on his newspaper. When he returned home in the evenings, he would shut himself in his room and work on his dictionary, his lips clamped and his eyes lusterless.

The house was bleak and lonely. The mother was gone, and the light of the house had vanished with her.

Every night Ben-Zion had nightmares. In his dreams he saw his mother lying on a bed, and men wearing black robes were coming to take her away. He shouted at them to leave her, not to take her; he begged her not to leave him alone, but they did not hear him. They went off slowly, taking his mother with them. He ran after them as fast as he could, and when he reached them his mother would look straight through him—as if he were a stranger. She did not recognize him, did not open her arms to him. She looked at him with indifference and went away, vanishing, never even turning her head to look back at him.

One night he woke up from a nightmare and suddenly it seemed to him that his mother's death was only a bad dream. She was probably only lying in bed. He got out of his bed, excited and hopeful, and rushed to his mother's room. But when he found the large bed empty, he fell upon it and wept for a long time.

The next day Eliezer removed Dvorah's bed from the house. Ben-Zion stood on the spot where the bed used to be and did not move. His head ached, and when he swallowed there was a terrible constricting pain in his throat. His grandmother gave him a glass of hot milk, and when he drank it his throat seemed to be on fire. "Are you sick, my little treasure?" the old woman asked anxiously, touching his forehead. He seemed very hot to her touch. The doctor was immediately called in. After he finished examining Ben-Zion, he looked very serious.

"The boy has diphtheria," he said. "There is an epidemic of diphtheria in Jerusalem, and hundreds of children are sick with it. It is a very dangerous sickness." Then he went on to examine the other children and found that Avichayil, Atara, and Shlomit had also contracted the terrible sickness.

Yemima was the only one whose throat was free from infection. "She must immediately be taken out of the house to avoid infection," the doctor ordered. "I

*Ben-Zion as a university student (about 1900)*

am going to take her across to the neighbors', where she will remain until the epidemic is over. They do not have children from whom she can catch it."

Three days later Avichayil died. The sturdy, happy, energetic boy lay quietly on his bed without moving. That evening Atara, the beautiful baby, died too. Shlomit's condition was very grave. She gurgled and her face was blue, for she could not breathe. She gripped her grandmother's hands as though begging for help. But there was nothing her grandmother could do for her. At midnight the child ceased breathing. Now there were three small bodies in the house.

Eliezer was dazed as he followed the three bodies which were borne by the burial society. The whole town of Jerusalem was numb with the shock and pain —for two thousand children had died from the epidemic. Every home was in mourning for a loved one, and the sound of crying rose from every house. The Ben-Yehudah family had suffered a triple blow. Three small graves were dug at the foot of the mother's grave. Eliezer was on the verge of collapse. He became sick. His cough choked him, and he grew very thin. A rumor went around Jerusalem that his days were numbered.

There were many people who were sorry for the grieving family, but there were many who rejoiced at their misfortune. . . . "We shall finally be rid of the heretic and his family," said his enemies.

"This is a fitting punishment for the infidel who speaks the holy tongue and who insists on bringing salvation before the arrival of the Messiah," muttered some of the long-bearded Jews in the synagogues.

"You mustn't say that!" said one old Jew. "I hear that the Almighty has seated Dvorah along with our reverent mothers, Sarah, Rivkah, Rachel, and Leah. Don't talk this way about the righteous woman."

"God had pity on the righteous woman and only took her children after her death," said one bent old woman.

At night Ben-Yehudah sat at his son's bedside, battling with him for every breath, for his very life.

"If I lose this child," he whispered to the doctor, "there will be no reason for me to live. If all the hopes I have for this boy are ended, all my work will be undone. He is the first Hebrew child. Don't let him die. Please do something for him," he begged, the tears streaming down his thin face.

"I am told that there is a young doctor who has just arrived from Germany," the doctor told Eliezer. "He has a new and remarkable medicine against diphtheria. Many of the children who have taken it have recovered, but there are still many people who are afraid of anything new. Are you willing to let me try it?"

Eliezer agreed. That evening Ben-Zion received the new medicine. The father and the doctor stayed at his side all night. In the morning there was a marked improvement in the boy's condition. He opened his eyes and in a weak voice asked for some water.

"The child is saved!" announced the doctor. A week later Ben-Zion was up on his feet, but he was still very weak. He had lost a lot of weight.

Yemima was allowed to return home. Only two were left of the five Ben-Yehudah children.

Old Feigaleh had lost her mind from sorrow. She would mumble prayers all day long. She believed that the tragedies had befallen the family because they did not observe the Jewish Laws. She taught the children to pray and made them repeat the prayers all day long. She began letting Ben-Zion's earlocks grow and dressed the children in the long black clothes of very Orthodox Jewish children. She stopped addressing the children in Russian or broken Hebrew and resumed using her customary Yiddish. The Ben-Yehudah family was no longer a Hebrew-speaking family. Eliezer, who saw what was going on, was helpless, for he did not have the energy to object. He could see the first Hebrew family crumbling before his eyes.

One day Ben-Zion was playing his usual game: he would pile up mounds of earth in the shape of graves and place tombstones and write inscriptions in memory of his mother, brother, and sisters. Suddenly he overheard a conversation between his father and Nissim Bechar.

"I find it very strange," said Mr. Bechar, "that you have decided to marry Dvorah's sister, Pola, so shortly after her death."

"This was Dvorah's last wish," replied Eliezer. "She asked me to do so on her deathbed."

"I don't think it's a good idea, my friend," said Bechar. "Just think about it. Have you really got the right to take a girl who is so much younger than yourself, a girl who is only twenty years old, a pretty, well-educated girl, and make her care for your children? And what of your sickness? And your problems? After all, what can you offer her? Your troubles? Your poverty?"

There was silence. Ben-Zion left his "cemetery." The thought of a new mother appealed to him. He had heard a great deal about Imma's younger sister, his Aunt Pola. Everybody said she was beautiful and clever and good. It would be wonderful if she could be their mother.

"You may be right, Nissim," he heard his father's voice.

"But I want a new Imma!" Ben-Zion suddenly burst in on them. "Please, Abba, please bring Aunt Pola and make her our mother. Please!" he begged excitedly. "I am so lonely and miserable without a mother!" There were tears in his eyes.

"You see, Nissim, the children need a mother," Eliezer said quietly.

## * twenty

"Yemima! Yemima! We are going to have a new mother! Aunt Pola will come and be our new mother!" Ben-Zion rushed into the house, announcing the important news to his sister.

"A new mother?" the little girl wondered happily. "Will she stay till our own Imma returns, one day?"

"What was it you just said?" asked their startled grandmother. "Ben-Zion, what did you say?"

But the boy had already rushed off to the street to inform everybody he saw that Aunt Pola was soon coming over from Russia and that she would become his father's wife. In no time at all this became the chief topic of conversation for the gossips.

"That infidel Ben-Yehudah. So now he wants to take another wife, does he?"

"Another wife—another victim!"

"Not enough for him to have lost most of his family. He wishes to marry another woman."

"And a girl who is fourteen years younger than himself, at that!"

People were outraged. Ben-Yehudah was perplexed and confused. He wished to marry his sister-in-law, Pola, but he was unsure of his decision. He kept asking himself whether he had the right to pluck this young flower from its homeland and plant it in a foreign soil. From day to day he kept putting off the letter to Pola. Many weeks went by.

One day he received a warm, affectionate letter from Pola. She wrote about her home and her family, her studies at the Faculty of Science at the Moscow University, about the books she read, and about her thoughts. She inquired after his health, after the children and his old mother, and wondered how they were managing without a mother and a wife. Her letter was full of reminiscences of bygone days, of barely remembered conversations with her brother-in-law when he had lived with her family. At the end of her letter she wrote and asked Eliezer to suggest a Hebrew name to replace her Russian name, Pola.

That night Eliezer wrote a long letter to Pola. He could detect her affection between the lines, and his heart told him that he should ask for her hand in marriage, ask her whether she would consent to become his wife. In his letter he told her of his life's work, his ambitions, his family and children. He wrote of the desolation in the house, and asked her whether she would be willing to become his wife. "I suggest that you change your name to Chemdah—beloved. I also suggest that you change your last name to Ben-Yehudah. Would you?"

When he received her written consent, he informed the children, "I will soon go away to bring your new mother."

Once again the town was in an uproar, and people spoke of Ben-Yehudah's new folly. "It is a real scandal," cried his enemies and opponents.

Even his friends and admirers did not look favorably upon the event. Nissim Bechar still tried to deter him from the marriage. Loyal friends of the Hebrew language dreaded the impact of a woman who spoke no Hebrew on the first Hebrew-speaking home.

But it was the family doctor whose words affected Eliezer most. "You have a serious and infectious disease," he told him one day. "You infected Dvorah with it. You must not marry a young girl and endanger her life, too. Who knows how many years are still left to you? Do you intend to leave a young widow, looking after children who are not even her own?"

These words shocked Eliezer deeply. That night he sat down and wrote a long letter to Chemdah, explaining things just as they were. Her reply came back immediately. It was brief and to the point:

*My dear, please thank the doctor, in my name, for worrying about my future.*

*Tell him that I am deeply moved, but I am still going to marry you. I know that this was the last wish of my beloved sister, and I will do everything I can to carry it out. I will live at your side —even if it is only for a day or a month. Each hour I spend beside you will be an hour of joy for me.*

*With all my love,*
*Chemdah*

The house was like a perfumery. The walls were whitewashed. Shrubs and flowers were planted in the garden. The excited children kept asking when their new mother was coming.

Eliezer sailed to Odessa, the city in Russia where Chemdah and her parents were waiting for him. He spent many hours on the deck, wondering about Chemdah, trying to guess what she looked like. It was seven years since he had last seen her, a pretty thirteen-year-old. What would she look like now? He could remember some of their arguments. At that time she was very distant from the Jewish people and their problems, but he would talk and tell her about the history of their people. In their arguments she proved that she had a mind of her own. He could also remember her as a baby, when he used to pick her up in his arms. He smiled when he remembered how when she was five years old he had promised to marry her. That was the only way he could get her to stop crying. And now she would really be his wife. The events of life were strange indeed.

In Odessa, Chemdah waited with a palpitating heart, a sturdy twenty-year-old girl, blooming with youth and vitality.

"I am afraid I may not recognize him," she told her mother as they stood waiting at the pier in Odessa. "So many years have passed. I am so excited, Mother."

"Nobody is forcing you to marry him, darling," her mother said.

"But I want to," whispered Chemdah. "Do you remember Dvorah's last letter to me?"

"What did she write? You never showed me the letter."

"I thought you would object. Dvorah told me, 'My sister, if you wish to live like a queen, come and take my place. . . .' Queen! Chemdah Ben-Yehudah! I am so happy, Mother."

"I hope you will be happy for a long, long time," her father said, as he lifted his eyebrows doubtfully. "You are both slightly crazy and probably match each other perfectly. But life in Jerusalem is so difficult. It is full of poverty and misery and endless quarrels. Is this the kingdom Dvorah referred to?"

"I am prepared to face anything as long as I am with him," cried Chemdah.

Tears welled in the mother's eyes. This was the way Dvorah had spoken, with all the ardor of youth. Was she going to sacrifice both her daughters to Eliezer?

"The boat is arriving," called Vanya, Chemdah's young brother. "It is such a big boat! Where is Eliezer?"

Eliezer went down the gangway to the wharf. He

was dressed in European clothes, but he wore a red tarbush on his head—after the fashion of the East.

"What a funny hat," laughed Penina, Chemdah's youngest sister.

The excited Chemdah lowered her eyelids and gave him her hand. His hand was warm. She raised her eyes very slowly and looked at him. Then came the smile, and with it a flood of relief. "Chemdah, my child, how you have grown!" he murmured.

"And you haven't changed at all. It's only your hat which is so funny. Do take it off!"

"I will do anything you ask me," he said as he took off his tarbush. He was very proud of it, for to him it symbolized the return of the Jews to an oriental country.

That night Chemdah and Eliezer sat and talked till dawn. Eliezer was happy to discover that Chemdah was as intelligent and educated as he had hoped. They spoke Russian, for Chemdah did not know any Hebrew.

"You must learn Hebrew so that you can bring up my children and our future children," he told her.

"I will do it for your sake," she announced.

Two days later Chemdah and Eliezer, accompanied by the Yonas family, sailed to Palestine.

One spring morning a cable arrived at the house in Jerusalem. The words were in Hebrew written in Latin characters: BEN-ZION. WE HAVE ALL ARRIVED SAFELY. COME AND MEET US AT BAB-EL-WAD. FATHER.

"Yemima, come here quickly. Let us go to Moshiko, the driver, immediately," cried Ben-Zion. He was delighted at the news, but he was even more thrilled to have received his very first cable. He grabbed his sister by her hand and ran to the alley where the carriage stood. Eliezer had made arrangements with the driver before his departure.

A few hours later they reached Bab-El-Wad.

"I can see them! I can see them!" shouted Ben-Zion, pointing with his finger at a small group clustered by the roadside.

"They seem so strange," muttered his sister. "Where is the new Imma? Is she the one holding the samovar in her hand?"

"That one is the grandmother, stupid. Our mother's mother. And that man over there in the overcoat is our grandfather. There she is over there. There is our new mother," he said, pointing at the elegant young woman with the hat.

"She is so pretty." Yemima was delighted. The carriage approached the group.

Maybe she is going to turn out to be a real stepmother, thought Ben-Zion, suddenly frightened. He could remember all the stories he had heard and read about cruel stepmothers. But she is also my real aunt. I guess she will be good to me. He tried to calm himself. The carriage stopped at the side of the road. The two children hesitated for a moment and did not jump off immediately.

"Come down here, children," the father smiled at them. "Come and meet your grandparents. This is your Uncle Vanya, and this is your Aunt Penina. And this is your new mother."

Uncle Vanya and Aunt Penina? But they are still children, just like me, thought Ben-Zion. But he did not have time to stop and consider that matter. The young woman walked over and smiled at them.

"Come on, Ben-Zion and Yemima, do get off the carriage. And you don't have to call me Imma or Auntie, either. You had only one mother, and there is no one else who can take her place. Call me Amma, just as you say Abba." She spoke to the children in Russian, and Eliezer acted as her interpreter. The children felt instinctively that the woman facing them was a good person, one who had their interests at heart. She was not going to be a stepmother, Ben-Zion told himself as he jumped down from the carriage. He walked over to Chemdah and hugged her warmly, and Yemima followed him.

## * *twenty-one*

Chemdah Ben-Yehudah began making changes in her new home as soon as she arrived. There was a great deal that had to be done. This was not a warm home but a barren and cold habitation, with bits and pieces of furniture thrown together without taste or style. The corridor served as a dining room, the beds were strewn all over without any semblance of order, Eliezer's books and papers lay scattered around in every corner of the house. Neglect and dirt were evident in every corner. The children were neglected. They looked like little old people: thin, anemic, slow in speaking. They were not allowed to play outside with other children in the street. They were very unhappy little children. Ben-Zion dressed in dark clothes, long trousers, a wide-brimmed hat, and long earlocks that curled down under the hat. Four-year-old Yemima wore a long dress that was far too big for her, and her scraggly hair fell loosely down to her shoulders.

Chemdah's first action was to cut the children's hair. To the grandmother's great distress, she also cut Ben-Zion's earlocks. Then she cut Ben-Zion's trousers and sewed them up to resemble boys' trousers. She did the same thing to Yemima's dresses, taking them in, shortening them, combing her hair, and putting a bright red ribbon around her head. She bought the children two fashionable straw hats to protect them from the sun.

They seemed to change overnight. She set about turning them into laughing, happy children. She had brought a caseful of toys, games, and books, with her from Russia. When she gave Yemima the big doll, the child was frightened and burst out crying; she had never seen such a doll before. Chemdah taught her how to play with the doll and how to wash her and dress her, and soon the child learned to enjoy this new game. Chemdah taught them how to play with a ball and with stones; she taught them how to sing and dance. She would spend many hours of the day in the garden with the children, playing, singing, and dancing.

"Ben-Yehudah has a goat for a wife. She skips in the garden all day long," said the gossips. But Chemdah ignored their evil tongues.

She threw out the old furniture and began refurnishing the house according to her own taste. There was no spare money for this, but she was a thrifty housewife and could bargain with the best. She managed to buy Damascene furniture and Turkish and Persian carpets. She discovered old furniture which had been placed in storage, cleaned it, gave it a coating of oil, and polished it till it shone. She hung her own hand-embroidered curtains on the vaulted windows and placed colorful pillows on the sills. Soon the house was warm with color.

Every member of the family was assigned his own small corner. She arranged an attractive living room, put up shelves for books and toys, hung pictures on the walls, and placed flowers in brass bowls. Everything was done with good taste.

In no time at all the bleak house became a delightfully warm home. Soon it became a meeting place for men of culture and intellect. People would drop in to spend an evening with the Ben-Yehudahs. Some of them were painters, authors, doctors, politicians, journalists, and representatives of various consulates in Jerusalem. They used to discuss art, politics, and science.

There was one thing which upset Ben-Yehudah and hurt him deeply. The glory of Hebrew was lost, and his family was no longer a Hebrew-speaking family. Chemdah spoke no Hebrew, and their guests spoke French, Russian, and German. During the day there was a babble of languages at home. Grandpa, Grandma, Vanya, and Penina spoke Russian. Chemdah addressed the children in French, and old Feiga-leh spoke Yiddish. And the word spread. "He preaches Hebrew, yet foreign languages are the only ones which can be heard in his own home. Ben-

Yehudah should not preach things which he himself does not practice."

Eliezer was dejected and upset. What was he to do? He did not wish to make Chemdah's first months in the new country too difficult; nor did he want to estrange her from her culture and her mother tongue. On the other hand, what was going to happen to the Hebrew language?

He decided to shift the printing press to his house and reached an agreement with his printers to speak only Hebrew. Then he engaged a tutor for the children: Chaim the Syrian, who spoke fluent Hebrew. Chaim was to be the children's companion from the moment they came back from school; he was to address them only in Hebrew and correct all their errors. But the children preferred Chemdah's company and did not like the idea of spending all their free time with a man whose job was to supervise and correct their Hebrew.

Chemdah was fully aware of what was going on. She could see her beloved husband's eyes grow moody and knew that only she could remove his sadness. It was up to her to learn Hebrew.

She made up her mind. But it was not easy. She, a woman who spoke so many European languages fluently, found this Semitic language very difficult, for everything in it seemed upside down. Ben-Yehudah spent several hours a day teaching her. The first thing they did was to read the entire Book of Genesis. Then she began to learn ordinary words, such as spoon, table, chair. She would sit on a cushion at the windowsill, repeating the words until she would burst out crying in desperation. "I am never going to learn this language," she would say a dozen times a day. Yet she never mentioned her doubts to her husband.

She was a good pupil, and he was a very patient teacher. He corrected her mistakes when she confused genders and muddled the past and present tenses. She looked upon conjugation as upon some frightening fortress which she had to conquer—and was unable to. Yet, at times, when she listened to her sister, Penina, and her brother, Vanya, whose name had been altered to Yoseph, she would tell herself that if they could pick up the language merely by listening to it, then she too had to do it. Then she would settle down to study with greater determination than before.

One evening Chemdah entered Eliezer's room and with a glowing face she recited a short speech in Hebrew, which she had learned by heart. "Eliezer, I never believed that this day would actually come, but I must tell you something important. From now on I want you to speak to me only in Hebrew. I guess that if you speak slowly, I will be able to understand you. I don't promise always to reply in Hebrew, but I hope that one day I shall be able to do so."

Eliezer's eyes shone. "Thank you, my darling," he said.

Six months after Chemdah's arrival in the country she spoke only Hebrew and stopped speaking foreign languages. Her Hebrew was slow and labored, but it was Hebrew. And once more the sound of Hebrew filled the house, echoing from every corner. The children laughed at her broken Hebrew and corrected her mistakes. But she took everything in stride and did not mind them. She addressed everybody in Hebrew: the grocer, the oil-vendor, the post office clerk. Anybody who wished to talk to her and be in her company tried to understand her language. It was a strange sight watching Chemdah address Russians and Frenchmen in Hebrew, with an interpreter standing and translating everything that was being said. She acted as if she could not speak those languages.

Ben-Yehudah was very grateful to his young wife. One evening, when they stood in the garden watching the sunset, he said, "Chemdah, my love, we shall soon go on a trip through Palestine. We are going to have a belated honeymoon. I would like you to see what our country looks like. And there is another reason for this trip."

"What is it?" she asked.

"You have been in the country only six months, and you speak Hebrew already. There are many people who doubt the fact that an adult can learn new languages. I want to prove to these nonbelievers that you have done it. You have battled with Hebrew and overcome its difficulties. This is genuine proof that anybody who wants to can do it. Then there is another thing. I want to show off my beautiful and charming wife." He smiled affectionately.

"I would love to see the country. Where shall we go?"

"I will take you to the village of Rishon-le-Zion. We may even visit Petach Tikvah, Zichron-Yaakov, and Haderah, and perhaps even go up to the Galil. It will be a slow journey, as we can only travel by horse and carriage. There are no trains in the country yet."

When Ben-Zion heard that his parents were going on a trip through the country, he became angry and complained vigorously. He told his young aunt, Penina, "Why don't they take me along? Why do they act like royalty and treat me like their slave? And this Chemdah, suddenly she begins to to order us about— as if father's bossiness was not enough for us. When my real mother was alive, she always gave in to my wishes, but Chemdah just interferes. She is always telling me what to wear, how to eat, and even expects me to wash myself daily. I never used to wash myself regularly, and especially not in such cold weather. And she even picks and chooses my friends—'Play with this one but keep away from that one.' What does she think I am, anyway? Her baby or something? And as if that is not enough for her, she had to go to my school. When she did not like my teachers she decided I had to leave the school and together with you, Penina, have a private tutor and study at home. And father never treats her the way he treated my mother. Whenever she wants anything he does it immediately."

"Maybe that's what really annoys you," laughed Penina wisely. "From your anger I can see that actually you love Chemdah very much, but perhaps the memory of your mother does not let you admit it, and that is why you are annoyed with your father for loving her and doing the things she wants him to. . . . The first thing you have to do is to admit to yourself that you love Chemdah and that you feel good when she is around. Then you will realize that you are not mad at her anymore. You will see that you are not even mad at your father any longer."

"But why don't they take me with them? After all, I am the first Hebrew child and I still haven't seen my country," Ben-Zion said, breaking into her words and coming out with the thing that was really bothering him. In his heart he was a little shocked by her accurate evaluation, but like any young boy, he preferred not to let on that he knew just how clever she was.

"That's the first sensible thing you've said this morning," said Penina. "I think that you ought to tell them what's on your mind and ask them to take you with them."

"Do you think they will?"

"It's worth trying. What have you got to lose?"

Ben-Zion ran to Chemdah and told her what he wanted. She immediately agreed to ask Eliezer to take him along. "I don't think he will have any objections." she said.

This time Ben-Zion was not at all angry with his father for carrying out all Chemdah's wishes.

One fine day during the Festival of Succot, Chemdah, Eliezer, and Ben-Zion left Jerusalem in a carriage, and headed for Rishon-le-Zion.

## * twenty-two

Ben-Zion sat in front, next to the driver, with a whip in his hand, thrilled at being able to point out the way. This was the third time he was leaving Jerusalem by carriage. He called out the names of the important sites and road signs and answered Chemdah's questions with an air of great importance.

"This is Shaar Hagai," he exclaimed. "This is where we first met, remember, Amma? And over there you can see an Arab village, right, Feivel?" He turned to the driver for assurance.

"Quite right," replied Feivel, the driver. "We must go through the village because I want to buy some fodder for the horses." He led his horses to the narrow pass leading to the village.

"Eliezer, do people actually live here?" Chemdah was quite shocked when she saw the place, a poor, miserable, tiny village, a few mud huts without any paint or plaster.

"Abba, Amma! Look at this! These houses have no windows at all!" excaimed Ben-Zion. "How can people breathe inside?"

When they entered one of the houses they discovered that it was, indeed, very difficult to breathe inside such a house. The room they stood in was dark and stifling. "Welcome, welcome," Saleem, Feivel's friend, greeted them. "Do sit down and have a cup of coffee, my friends."

They sat on a mat on the floor, leaning against colored cushions. On a coal brazier in the middle of the room, Saleem boiled the coffee in a sooty coffeepot known as a *finjan,* while goats, hens, and dogs roamed about inside the room, followed by a few half-dressed, bleary-eyed children with dripping noses.

"These children look terrible," Chemdah whispered to Eliezer. "They are so filthy and sick-looking."

Eliezer signaled to Chemdah to keep quiet. The

Arab understood some Hebrew, and Eliezer did not wish to offend him. Slowly they sipped sweet coffee from the miniature coffee cups. "Thank you very much, my friend," Eliezer said to his host as he rose to his feet. "We still have a long journey ahead of us." They left the stifling room and breathed deeply the fresh air outside.

"They heat their stoves with horse manure," explained Eliezer. "This adds a terrible stench to the stifling atmosphere inside."

The women were sitting on the threshold of their homes, grinding wheat in the same way it had been done for thousands of years. Chemdah waved to them from the carriage, and they smiled and looked at her with curiosity as they whispered to each other. She was as strange to them as they were to her.

After many hours of plodding along in the sands of the lowlands, Eliezer suddenly called out, "Look over there. A red roof. That must be the synagogue of Rishon-le-Zion. We are almost there."

When they reached the village, Chemdah was filled with surprise. This was not the village she had visualized. After having seen the Arab village, she thought she would meet a similar sight in Rishon-le-Zion. But what she saw were white, blue, and pink houses—like flowers planted in rows in a garden. The dry, sandy scenery had changed as if by magic, and everything here was fresh and green. Vines and trees grew in abundance.

"This is the Hebrew village!" Eliezer announced formally. "This is our soil. The desert has become a place of habitation!"

"What a wonderful sight," whispered the excited

and bewildered Chemdah. "I have never seen such a lovely village before." The carriage drove slowly down the street, and its passengers looked around, enchanted.

"Where are these people going, Abba?" asked Ben-Zion, pointing at the men who were walking in one direction with parcels in their hands.

"They are going to the public bath, to get washed and ready for the Sabbath. It will soon be Sabbath, my son. Well, we've arrived. Here is David's house, where we are going to spend the Sabbath."

The family stepped down from the carriage, took their leave from Feivel and walked across to a small, pale blue house. On the way they passed a group of children who were playing with a ball. Ben-Zion stopped to watch them for a moment.

"Abba!" he called out, when he caught up with his father. "They are playing in Hebrew! I heard them call out to one another—'Let me have it!' 'Catch!' 'It's your turn now!' " Ben-Zion's face shone as if he had discovered a big treasure.

"Yes, my son," replied his father. "Here, in Rishon-le-Zion, a generation of Hebrew-speaking children is being raised. One day all the children and adults in this country will speak only Hebrew. In Rishon, they are taking the first steps on this long and difficult journey."

Friday evening was spent with the family of David, the village teacher. After supper the house was filled with guests. Everybody wanted to meet Ben-Yehudah, about whom they had heard so much. To Eliezer's delight and to Chemdah's joy, for now she could take an active part in the conversation, everybody spoke only Hebrew.

"Six months in the country and you speak so fluently?" whispered one of the women in Russian. "Look at me. I have been living here for ten years, and I still cannot speak much. There is so much work on the farm and around the house, and with the children and their sicknesses," she said apologetically.

"I am sorry," Chemdah replied in Hebrew. "I don't understand a word."

"Would you like me to be your interpreter?" asked one of the young men.

"This is really funny," whispered Ben-Zion to his father. "She acts as if she really does not understand a word, and the man has to repeat everything that woman says. What a funny show," he said, smiling.

The women gathered around Chemdah. They wanted to talk to her and admire her Hebrew, her pretty dress, and her fresh and lovely complexion.

In the beginning Ben-Zion listened to the talk about the village of Haderah and its terrible fate—how all its inhabitants had died of malaria and nobody was left there at all—and how the place seemed like one large cemetery. But when the conversation shifted to the newspaper *Hatzvi* and the Ben-Yehudah dictionary, he became bored and slipped out of the house. It was an autumn evening. There was a breeze in the air which carried a whiff of the freshly ploughed fields. He could hear children shouting in the distance, and he followed the sound.

"I am Ben-Zion Ben-Yehudah from Jerusalem," he said, introducing himself.

"Your father is Ben-Yehudah?" they asked. Their voices did not contain the note of sneering which he was accustomed to hearing from boys his age in

Jerusalem. On the contrary, their voices were full of admiration and even envy. They were jealous of him for being the son of the famous Ben-Yehudah.

"Want to join us, Ben-Zion?" they asked. "We are going to the barn. Do you think your folks will let you come along?" Ben-Zion clambered over the highest bundle of straw and rolled down, shouting gleefully with the other children. It was so good here, in this quiet village, it was so peaceful and warm and friendly. Nobody laughed at him for speaking Hebrew. They were all his friends.

When the sound of singing was heard, the children picked themselves up and cleaned the straw from their clothes. "Come along," they told Ben-Zion. "They've started singing and dancing. They're really enjoying themselves over there. Let's go and join them."

Everybody was having a good time in the David house. People sang and danced until dawn.

On Saturday the family strolled through the village. They breathed the peaceful air of the cultivated fields and rows of vines. Ben-Zion would have loved to stay in the village a little longer and play with his new friends. But Ben-Yehudah was in a hurry to be off.

"I am afraid we have to cut our trip short this time. There is a great deal of work waiting for me in Jerusalem. Only yesterday did I begin to understand just how important my dictionary really is. I must provide words for the people who wish to speak Hebrew. This is no time for journeys and sightseeing. Time is short and there is much to be done."

"But Abba," said Ben-Zion angrily, "you promised we would go to so many places."

"Some other time, my son," said Eliezer. Then he realized how badly upset and disappointed the boy was. "Do you know what?" he said. "Tomorrow the train will leave Jaffa on its first journey to Jerusalem. Would you like to go home by train?"

Ben-Zion's eyes shone. To travel by train? For that he was quite willing to forgo the rest of the journey.

When they reached Jaffa, Chemdah, who was accustomed to European trains, soon saw that this train was only an old steam engine with three small carriages. To her it seemed more like a toy than a train. But Ben-Zion, who had only seen pictures of trains, was thrilled and excited.

"Does the train really travel by itself, without horses? You mean to say that we can actually reach Jerusalem this evening by train? So quickly?"

They climbed up the stairs. The carriages moved —a slight shifting movement—and the train was on its way.

"It's going so fast!" exclaimed Ben-Zion, standing at the window with the wind blowing through his hair.

"What's this? What happened? Why has the train stopped?" cried Ben-Zion when the train halted half an hour later.

When they looked out the window they saw a strange sight. Arab horsemen were standing on the rails with their horses and donkeys and would not move. They were shouting and gesticulating and screwing up their faces in fury.

"What do they want?" asked Chemdah. "Why are they so angry?"

Eliezer listened to what was being said, and explained. "They claim that the 'horseless carriage'—as they call the train—is the devil's work; that it is a demon running with its smoke blowing. They are not prepared to let this demon pass close to their village. They are afraid it is evil. I had better go down and explain it to them."

Eliezer spent a long time with the excited Arabs. Finally the Arabs agreed to get off the rails and let the train continue its journey.

"It is not easy to switch over from the age of the camel to a modern train," sighed Eliezer, wiping his forehead tiredly, as he climbed back to his carriage.

The engine moved on through the mountains. Ben-Zion was very impressed by its strength, which enabled it to carry such a load and did not make it necessary for anyone to get off and push it uphill.

"Why do they stop every other minute?" he asked his father. "Whenever anybody stands on the rails and signals to them, the engine driver stops to pick him up. I can't stand it."

"This doesn't happen on most trains," Chemdah explained. "Real trains have proper stations and regular timetables. Our train must be a particularly good one, because it tries to satisfy everybody."

"The day will come, Chemdah dear," said Eliezer, "when we, too, shall have fast trains, just as they do in Moscow. One day the journey from Jaffa to Jerusalem will take only a few hours. By that time Jerusalem will be a proper city with factories, fine shops, and busy streets. Other large towns will also spring up in this country, and there will be many villages all over. One day this desert will become a fertile land—the land of the Jews. They will return from everywhere to their homeland. They will come back to the Hebrew language from seventy different tongues."

Ben-Zion looked at his father. Suddenly he appeared to him like a prophet of old, as he stood there with his reddish pointed beard and his eyes glittering with the fervor of his belief.

"The day will come . . . the day will come . . . the day will come . . . ," sang the wheels of the train.

## * twenty-three

Shortly after his return to Jerusalem, Ben-Zion gathered Penina, Yoseph, and Yemima around him and began telling them about the Hebrew villages and the train journey. He told them the things he had heard from the youngsters and the adults. The children drank in his words, asked questions, and begged him to continue telling them about his adventures. It was getting very late, but nobody seemed tired or wanted to go to sleep.

"The children in Rishon-le-Zion told me that six months ago, the Arab guards who patrol the vineyards killed one of the local Jewish farmers. These Arabs are not to be trusted. The farmers take them on as guards and watchmen, and pay for their work. Now just see what they are up to."

"What?" asked Yoseph.

"They open the gates wide to the robbers and murderers. There have been a number of such instances."

"Why don't the Jews guard their own vineyards?" asked Yemima.

"How can Jews be guards?" inquired Penina.

"Why not?" Ben-Zion replied excitedly. "Nobody believed that Jews would ever make good farmers, and you see now that they can. Why not have a Jewish army, too? An army which would protect the villages, lives, and property of the Jews. An army. A regular army, like the ones the Israelites had in the days of King David and King Saul. An army like we had in the times of the Maccabees. A Jewish army!"

"But what for?" wondered Yoseph. "After all, the Turkish army is here to make sure that we have peace and order."

"But the Turks are strangers. We need our own army. A real army!" Ben-Zion became very excited and stood up. "Come on, let's go and start a Jewish army. I will be the commanding officer, and you will be the soldiers."

"Yes, that's a good idea," agreed Yemima.

Yoseph and Penina were not so happy with the idea, but Ben-Zion was already busy with his plans. "We'll call for an urgent meeting tomorrow. We can invite a few of the other children, and they can bring along some of their friends. I'm going to write to the children of Rishon. I'm sure they'll be delighted to join us. We'll begin to train with weapons. . . ."

"I don't believe this idea of yours is any good at all," said Yoseph, sneering slightly.

Left: Leah Aboushdid, "The Belle of Jerusalem," at the time of her engagement to Ben-Zion

Below: Mrs. Leah Ben-Avi on their honeymoon

"On the contrary, I am just beginning to like this idea," said Penina.

"Let's go to sleep now," said Ben-Zion. "Tomorrow evening we'll meet under the palm tree in our garden. Penina, you better make sure that the children I suggested are there on time. Everybody must be there at eight o'clock sharp."

It was a moonlit evening when the new "Jewish army" met for the first time. Ben-Zion was elected commander in chief, Yoseph became a major, Penina and Yemima were made captains, and all the other children present became sergeants.

"From now on, anybody who joins us will be an ordinary soldier," decided Ben-Zion.

They stayed in the garden till late at night, discussing training methods, mobilization of soldiers, uniforms, a flag, and the additional details which no self-respecting army can ever do without.

"Well, now come the financial problems," sighed Ben-Zion when all the other issues had been cleared up. "Where are we going to get the money?"

"We shall all bring something from our homes, and then we'll have some money," suggested Chaim.

"It will be a drop in the bucket," said Yoseph. "We need more, much more."

"I have an idea!" Ben-Zion jumped up. "A great idea! Just listen to me! We shall send a letter to Baron Rothschild. He is a very rich and generous man. He donates money to all sorts of causes. He built a large public bath in Rishon-le-Zion. I saw it myself. And he also supports Abba's newspaper. I am sure that if we write and tell him about our idea for a Jewish army, he will send us enough money to keep us going."

"But we don't even know his address," said Baruch.

"I do!" said Ben-Zion. "He lives in Paris, in France. Everybody there must know him. Our teacher told us that he lives in a castle. And if he lives in a castle, it is probably near the castle of the president of the Republic. I am going to sit down and write to him tomorrow, as soon as we've decided just how much money we'll need. And remember, we're all meeting tomorrow near the wall for basic training. Tomorrow at four—and everybody had better be there on time. Remember—not a word to anybody!"

"But we'll never have uniforms and weapons ready by tomorrow," exclaimed Simcha.

"It doesn't matter. For the time being we'll train without weapons."

The children departed with a smart salute and went to their homes. But sleep was far away from the first "Jewish soldiers" that night. They were too excited.

At four o'clock the next afternoon, the officers and the sergeants sat next to their commanding officer and listened to his briefing. "I have checked everything. I've planned the uniform and have even found a tailor who is willing to sew them for us. This evening I'm going to design our flag. I have even written an anthem and prepared a letter to Baron Rothschild. All you have to do now is simply sign it, and everything will be in order."

"I think that you ought to read the letter to us," said Penina.

Ben-Zion removed a folded sheet of paper from

his pocket with great formality. He opened it and began to read solemnly:

*The Honourable Baron Edmund de Rothschild*
*Paris Castle (near the Castle of the President)*
*Paris, France*

> *Please do not be surprised by this letter from your obedient servant. The recent incidents in a number of Your Honor's villages, when a few farmers were killed by Arab "guards," caused worry and upheaval among the Jews of this country. For this reason, I, the undersigned, on behalf of many of my friends, girls and boys, numbering a few hundred*

"But that's a lie," interrupted Yoseph. "There are only eight of us."

"There will be more of us by the time he receives this letter. Anyhow, it's not all that important!" Ben-Zion was furious at the interruption and read on quickly:

> *This is why the undersigned addresses Your Highness with a suggestion, which may at first seem rather daring to you. I am prepared to take upon myself the responsibility of creating a Jewish army. This army will protect the villages of Your Highness. In the beginning the army should number 100 people. According to my estimate we shall need a sum of 100 gold francs per month for this project.*
> *We have begun our training, and even have*

*a flag with the following inscription:* THE FLAG OF
THE CAMP OF JUDAH OF THE ARMY OF ISRAEL. *Our uniform is to be green—the color of the vineyards. I
have translated the first verse of the* Marseillaise
*into Hebrew and it will serve as our anthem.*

*In days of old we had people like Samson, the
Maccabees, and men like Bar-Kochba. Why
should we not have people like the Rothschilds
today? Indeed, this is what we shall name our
soldiers. Send us your reply with the requested
donation, for then your name will go down in the
annals of Israel, not merely as the generous
baron, but as the chief of staff of the army of
Israel. We would be much obliged if you could
send us the first 100 francs by return mail, to
enable us to pay for our officers' uniforms.*
*King Saul smote thousands;*
*Your Highness will smite tens of thousands.*

*With great humility,*
*Ben-Zion Ben-Yehudah*
*Colonel in the Jewish Army*

Everybody was quite impressed by the letter.

"We must make sure that there are no spelling
mistakes," said Penina. "It would make a terrible impression if there should be any mistakes in it."

"There are no mistakes. Everything is in order.
All you have to do now is sign your names here, just
below my name."

"I think that your signature is enough. After all,
you are the commander," said Chaim.

"He's right!" everybody agreed.

"I want to have nothing to do with this business. You are not going to get any money. It's only going to cause trouble," said Yoseph, and he rose and left the group.

"I want to be a major instead of him," volunteered Baruch.

"According to the order of seniority, Penina should become major. You can become a captain in her place," decided the commander. "Yoseph can go if he wants to. There will be twenty others to fill his place. Let's go to the post office now and mail this letter. Form a line behind me, and I will sing our anthem. You can join me. You all know the tune—it's the tune of the *Marseillaise*. Forward, march!"

> *Come along, you children of the homeland,*
> *For the day of glory has arrived!*
> *For Araby will face us*
> *With a banner of blood.*
> *To arms, citizens, to arms!*

Ben-Zion was singing at the top of his lungs, and the children accompanied him by humming the familiar tune.

"Sing, soldiers! Sing loudly!" he ordered. "Raise your heads high and march like officers. That's the spirit! Left, right, left, right!"

People watched the children marching along the street and singing the *Marseillaise*.

Everybody is thrilled with us, thought Ben-Zion. They like our song. And when they find out about the Jewish army they will really think the world of us. Yoseph is going to be very sorry that he left us. Still,

I'll take him back, but only as an ordinary soldier. Maybe if he proves himself, I'll make him a sergeant. In a year's time.

The post office clerk looked at the envelope, read the strange address, raised his eyebrows, and asked, "Do you have your father's permission to send this letter?"

"It's all right," replied Ben-Zion. "The baron will be delighted to receive the letter." His self-confidence and air of importance acted like a charm, and the letter was dispatched.

Now began a period of anxious waiting for the reply and the money. The army went on training regularly—but without uniforms and weapons it seemed like a child's game to them. They used sticks instead of rifles. They tried to persuade the tailor to sew the green uniforms on credit, but he refused, saying, "I have to buy the material, and I need money for that. I shall sew your uniforms as soon as you are able to pay me."

Days passed, weeks and months went by. One day the baron's representative turned up at the Ben-Yehudah home. He was furious with Eliezer, and told him, "So! Ben-Yehudah is up to his old tricks, is he now? The baron has instructed me to tell you that if you are capable of such tricks in order to extract more money out of him, he can no longer trust you at all."

"What are you talking about?" asked Eliezer in surprise.

"About your letter to the baron, of course," replied the representative. "You have no idea what a terrible impression it made on him. A Jewish army! I have never heard anything so foolish before!"

"But, sir—"

"No buts. The baron has instructed me to tell you that you have disappointed him gravely. He has decided to stop supporting your paper. He—"

"Please, sir," Chemdah came to her husband's aid. "I am sure that the whole business must be due to some misunderstanding. Do you happen to have this letter with you?"

The man took the letter out of his briefcase and handed it to her without a word.

The letter was read. A terrible uproar shook the house.

"How could you do this to me?" shouted Eliezer to his son, gripping his shoulders and shaking him till his teeth rattled.

"I wrote the letter. We must have a Jewish army. If the baron isn't willing to help us, we'll do it ourselves, without his help!"

"Oh, Ben-Zion, you're such a baby," intervened Chemdah. "Do you actually understand what you're saying?"

"Since when have children begun to mix in adult affairs?" demanded the representative.

Who knows how this matter would have ended had not an unexpected event taken place at that moment. Suddenly Chemdah's face contorted in pain.

"Eliezer! I think I am about to give birth. Go and get the midwife."

Ben-Zion made the most of this opportunity and rushed outside. He spent the entire day in the streets, upset and dejected about the wonderful plan which had no backing. When he came home in the evening, Yemima ran over to him and informed him, "Ben-

Zion, Amma has given birth to a little girl. She's a beautiful little baby. And we are going to call her Dvorah, after our own mother."

# * *twenty-four*

The new baby brought peace and serenity to the turbulent home. Eliezer, who was delighted with the little child, did not mention Ben-Zion's "crime" again. The letter was forgotten and nobody ever brought up the incident. The house was again filled with the sounds of an infant's cries and chuckles, with joy over the first word and delight over the first footsteps.

Happiness reigned in the house.

But Ben-Yehudah's enemies in Jerusalem were very busy. They discovered a new reason to tear Ben-Yehudah to pieces, and they jumped at the opportunity. The matter was talked about for a long time.

"That son of the infidel, Ben-Yehudah, has sent a letter to the baron."

"He is thinking of creating a Jewish army! Have you ever heard anything of the sort in your life?"

"This is not the boy's idea. He must have heard such talk in his father's home."

"That's right. That man and his fancies are going to be disastrous for all of us!"

"First he tells us that we must stop receiving our 'allowances' from abroad, which enable us to study the Torah and not have to work. Then he tells us to go out to work. And now this brand-new idea: a Jewish army! That's all we need—to have the Turkish authorities hear this story and charge us with rebellion."

About a year later—Chemdah had just given birth to her second child, a son named Ehud—an article was published in the Hanukkah issue of *Hatzvi* describing the bravery of the Maccabees. This time the enemies of Ben-Yehudah did more than talk. They went to the Turkish authorities. They spent a long time with the pasha of Jerusalem, listing all the alleged crimes of Ben-Yehudah. They said that the article about the Maccabees was only a ruse and that it was really an incitement to revolt against the Turks. They informed the pasha about Ben-Yehudah's plans for returning the land of Israel to the Jews, and about his son's effort to create a Jewish army to take the place of the Turkish army and perhaps even fight it. They told him of the notorious letter to the baron, the training of the soldiers, the anthem, and the uniforms. For some reason, however, they neglected to mention that the leader of the army was an eleven-year-old boy.

When the Turkish pasha heard all this he was furious and ordered the immediate arrest of Ben-Yehudah. His men broke into the Ben-Yehudah home, threw his books around, tore up pages and sheets of paper which they found on the desk, and searched for some evidence of the man's rebellion.

Ben-Yehudah was bewildered. "What is it?" he asked. "What are you looking for?"

The soldiers did not reply. The noise brought Chemdah from her bed. It was four days since she had given birth. She entered the room, a pale woman with an infant in her arms. Dvorah, the year-old baby, was clinging to her skirts.

"What are you doing in my house?" she demanded angrily. "Stop it immediately!"

The soldiers pushed her aside roughly. Little Dvorah was very frightened and began crying loudly. One of the soldiers took a pair of handcuffs from his pocket and shackled Ben-Yehudah. Then they ordered him to come with them.

"What has he done? Why are you arresting him?" Chemdah called after them. They did not reply.

Ben-Yehudah was placed in a police van and was taken to the Central Prison of the Old City.

Chemdah got dressed and went to Nissim Bechar for advice.

Ben-Zion was at school when this happened. When school was over, he set off for home. His way was blocked by a group of yeshiva boys. He remembered a forgotten scene—the way his dog Speedy had been stoned.

"Let me pass," he said quietly.

The boys, who were older and bigger than Ben-Zion, would not let him pass. They danced around him and sang a strange song. They sang it in Hebrew, to make sure that he understood every word. "Your father is in prison! He has received his punishment! Your father, the infidel, the rebel, is in prison!"

"What happened to him?" Ben-Zion was terribly upset. "In prison? What for?"

"You will never see him again as long as you live.

The rebel was sentenced to death," was the cruel jeer.

"My father is not a criminal! That's not true! You're lying! Lying!" screamed the boy.

"Who does he think he is, calling us liars?" cried one of the boys, and landed a heavy fist in Ben-Zion's face. The circle closed around him. Soon a shower of boots and fists rained on the boy.

A sickening thought flashed through his head. They will kill me just the way they killed my dog. He tried to slide and slip through their legs, but the wall of bodies fenced him in.

"Help! Somebody help me! They are killing me!" he shouted at the top of his voice. But his screams were lost in the noise. He knelt on the ground and covered his head with his hands for protection. He could feel the salty taste of blood. He tried desperately not to cry. From time to time he tried to hit back, but with little effect.

Suddenly there was silence. The beating stopped. He looked up and saw Chemdah standing over him. He stood up immediately, dirty, tattered, and full of bruises.

"What have they done to you, child?" she asked, hugging him closely.

Ben-Zion wept in her arms. The tears which he had kept back until now burst like a dam.

"What heroes!" Chemdah said scornfully. "As soon as they saw me coming, they ran away. I happened to pass here by mere chance."

"They said that Abba was in prison and that he has been sentenced to death. Tell me they're lying, Amma!"

Chemdah tried to control herself. She took Ben-

Zion's hand and walked down the street with him. "Your father *is* in prison, Ben-Zion. I am on my way back from the pasha. People have told the authorities that he is a rebel. There was a search in our house a few hours ago, and he was arrested. We are now on our way to prison, and I hope we will be allowed to see him." She took a handkerchief out of her bag and wiped his bloody, tear-stained face.

"I am going to tell Abba about the boys. They beat me up, but they spoke to me in Hebrew. In good Hebrew, not a word in Yiddish. He will be very pleased, won't he?"

"They did not do that because they love Hebrew, but because they hate us. They wanted to make sure you understood what they were saying," said Chemdah. Ben-Zion's face had begun to swell and the bruises had turned blue. He was limping slightly.

"Does it hurt you badly?" she asked, pressing his hand.

"Their words hurt me more. They always say the same nasty things. They hate us, all of us; but they hate Abba worst of all. But we'll never give in to them, Amma. Not even if they beat us or send us to prison."

"Your father will be very happy to hear you speaking like this, my dear." Chemdah smiled at him affectionately. Ben-Zion felt that he was an adult, a young man standing by his father's side, a partner and an ally in his battles. This cheered him up and made him forget the injuries and the insults.

There was a small grille at the large iron gate of the prison. A sleepy face peered out of it. Chemdah explained her mission, but the man would not let her enter. He pretended not to understand a word. Only after she placed a few silver coins in his hand did he seem to grasp her intention. He opened the gate.

The prison warden led the way. He took them to the cell in which Ben-Yehudah was locked. Ben-Zion was shocked when he saw the cell—a dirty, narrow, mildewed hole which contained three prisoners lying on the floor, chained to the wall. The light filtered through a tiny window high up in the cell. Chemdah and Ben-Zion stood near the window and looked for Eliezer. When their eyes grew accustomed to the dark, they could make out his slight body, lying near the wall.

"At least they haven't chained him, as they did the others," whispered Chemdah.

"Abba, Abba!" called Ben-Zion. "What have they done to you? Why have you been imprisoned?"

Eliezer raised his head and walked slowly over to the window. His face had altered considerably. He was pale and looked very ill. "They are not going to keep me in here for long, child. Don't worry about me. They are not going to be able to accuse me falsely."

"The visit is over," announced the warden. Ben-Zion's requests and Chemdah's pleas were of no use. They had to leave.

"Don't worry," Eliezer consoled them. "I will return home today. They will realize that they have made a mistake and will let me go."

But it was a week before Ben-Yehudah was discharged from prison. The damp and stifling cell was very bad for his frail health. He was unable to eat the wormy food. Chemdah visited him daily and took him food and cheered him up. Each day Ben-Zion would rush home from school, burst into the house, and ask, "Has Abba been released yet?"

One gray, rainy afternoon, Ben-Zion returned from school and found his father at home. "Have they let you go?" he asked happily.

Eliezer's face was very grave.

"Yes, they have—but only because of a very big bribe. I had to borrow money from many people. Who knows when we shall ever be able to return it?"

"Who thinks of money?" said Chemdah. "The main thing is that you are back home."

"But they forbade me to publish the paper at least for a year. An entire year of forced silence! Do you realize what it means for me?"

"Yes. It is terrible. But you should look at the happy side of things. You can devote yourself entirely to your dictionary. Maybe you will even finish it. Many people are looking forward to its completion."

Chemdah tried to cheer him up, but she too was very depressed. They were deep in debt, and now that the paper could no longer be published their income would be cut drastically.

They went through a very difficult winter. There were heavy rains and strong gales. Eliezer would move about silently, like a caged lion. Without his work on the paper, he seemed paralyzed. His health deteriorated, and he was coughing constantly and spitting blood. The people of Jerusalem would not visit the family because it was under suspicion by the authorities. They were poor and lonely.

One rainy winter night, Ehud, the baby, died. This was Chemdah's first encounter with death. The baby had contracted pneumonia in the morning, and by nightfall the tiny body was still. An additional grave, the fifth, was dug in the burial plot of the Ben-

Yehudah family. Chemdah's tears mingled with the
rain which lashed ruthlessly against their faces as
they walked down from the Mount of Olives.

## * *twenty-five*

After the funeral Ben-Zion could find no place for
himself in the bereaved and depressed house, and
finally he went out to the street. He walked aim-
lessly in the rain and the wind, until he started
shivering with cold. He did not have to attend
school, for this was still the period of the seven
days of mourning for his baby brother. He had no
idea where he was heading. He went through a
gate and continued walking down the narrow,
winding lanes until he found himself standing op-
posite Chajiz's tiny bookshop. He crossed the street
quickly and entered the dark shop. A small kerosene lamp flickered, and shadows fell on the gray
stone wall. There was a smell of paper and prin-
ter's ink in the air. Ben-Zion loved this shop with
its smell of old and new books, and he liked Chajiz,
the good-natured owner of the shop who used to let
him sit in a corner, browsing through the books.

"Ben-Zion, my lad." Chajiz seemed really happy
to see him. "I am very pleased you came. I must show
you something new. Here, have a look at this. I received it from Europe only yesterday!" He removed a

cover from a small machine which stood on the table. "This contraption is known as a hectograph."

"Oh yes. I heard about it. My father mentioned it once. He called it a copying machine. One can make many copies on it, isn't that right?"

"Quite right. Just write something on this piece of paper, and I will show you how the hecto—what was that name you used?"

"Copying machine."

"Let it be copying machine! Go on, write something. It makes no difference what you write. I am going to show you how this thing operates."

Ben-Zion wrote the first two lines of the anthem of the Jewish army in a large, clear script: "Come along, you children of the homeland,/For the day of glory has arrived!"

Chajiz placed the sheet in the machine, pressed the handle, and a clear copy appeared on the clean sheet. He pressed the lever once again—another copy, and another, and yet another.

"Well, Ben-Zion, what about it? I will let you have it cheap. You will be able to make copies of your song and distribute it all over Jerusalem. Would you like to buy it?"

Ben-Zion looked at the machine. He was tempted, and would have loved to buy it. There were so many possibilities with such a machine. It was like a small printing press. Why, he could even publish a small newspaper. . . . A paper! The idea took root and inflamed him. A paper for the children of Jerusalem. He would be able to write articles, short stories, and poems. His father would be so proud of the son who was following in his footsteps. Abba would also be able to write in it and once again find a forum for his ideas.

What a wonderful project!

"I'll buy it. Please keep it for me," he told Chajiz, and hurried out of the shop. He ran in the cold rain, but he was so full of new plans and ideas that he felt warm and flushed. He ran to the school and waited for his lessons to end. He waited for what seemed an eternity, until the bell rang and the children began pouring out of the schoolyard.

Ben-Zion watched the boys until he saw the one he was looking for, Baruch. He ran over to him immediately and told him of his plan.

"Think of it, Baruch! A children's paper. I'll be the editor, and you'll write the paper. You have the nicest handwriting in our class. Come with me to the Old City and see it for yourself. It's called a copying machine!"

"What paper are you talking about? What's a copying machine?" asked Baruch, trying to keep up with Ben-Zion.

"You'll soon see for yourself. We're going to publish a newspaper and we'll call it *The Boy*. All the children of Jerusalem, Jaffa, Rishon-le-Zion, and the other villages will read it. We'll be the owners. We'll be famous and rich, Baruch!"

Baruch slowly began to understand the idea and was very impressed by it. Now they faced the real problem. Where would they find the money to buy the machine?

That very evening the boys began a fund-raising campaign. Nissim Bechar, the schoolmaster, gave them the first donation. He approved of the idea. A few other people also donated some money. There were some who viewed the project favorably and gave a considerable sum of money; others gave only a small donation in order to get rid of the young nuisances.

Finally they were able to buy the machine. Chajiz gave them five hundred sheets of paper free with the machine, as well as some special ink. Now they had to get down to work. Ben-Zion thought he would write the articles and stories on his own, but after two days of hard and intensive work he decided to add Yehudah to the editorial board, for his Hebrew was good and his literary style excellent.

The boys spent many evenings working on their paper. Finally all the stories and articles were ready. Ben-Zion added a few riddles, a crossword puzzle, and some tongue twisters. All that was left now was the copying, the duplicating, and the distribution of the paper.

Baruch wrote out the name of the paper in large block letters :

THE BOY

"It's no good," said Yehudah. "After all, the paper is also intended for girls, isn't it?"

This seemed a reasonable objection, and the three began to think of another name. After much arguing and many discussions, they decided to name the paper

THE HEBREW LANGUAGE

The first sheet was thrown into the wastebasket, and Baruch rewrote the name in his large, clear handwriting: THE HEBREW LANGUAGE. This was followed by the contents:

1. Letter to the young reader
2. The task of the Hebrew-speaking children in our country
3. Only Hebrew—or French and Turkish too?
4. The borders of our country as promised to our forefathers
5. Eight-day tour of Israel
6. Various games
7. Children's newspapers in France
8. Crossword puzzle and riddles

The children gazed at the front page with pride as it left the copying machine. "It looks like a real newspaper," declared Yehudah in amazement.

"What did you think we were working on?" replied Ben-Zion, covering up his own delight with an air of sophistication. But finally he was unable to restrain his impatience. "How much more is there to copy?" he asked Baruch. He was eager to finish his paper.

The boys spent a week on the paper. At last the great moment arrived, and the first issue of *The Hebrew Language,* copied by Baruch and duplicated in the copying machine, was ready. Yehudah wrote all the literary articles; the other articles were prepared by Ben-Zion. All that was left now was to sell and distribute the paper.

On Thursday afternoon, Yehudah, Baruch, and Ben-Zion started roaming all over town selling the newspaper. They went from house to house, talking and cajoling cheerfully, trying to find people interested in their cause.

"Sir, please buy the first issue of the new children's paper, *The Hebrew Language.* It will be a wonderful gift for your children."

"Madam, the paper will help your children with their Hebrew studies. It will turn them into better citizens. If you sign for a year's subscription, each issue will only cost you a few pennies."

"The first children's paper to be published in Jerusalem!"

"Children writing for children!"

Some people smiled and bought the paper from the delighted children. Others banged the door in the editors' faces and occasionally even added a string of curses. A number of yeshiva students in the Old City rushed to buy the paper to see what new trick the son of Yudke the infidel was up to.

The boys walked for hours. They were hungry and thirsty but elated over their success.

"We have already sold seventy-five copies!" announced Yehudah when he calculated their earnings. "It's not at all bad for a start."

"Can we continue tomorrow?" asked Baruch, who was very tired.

"Let's only go to the post office," said Ben-Zion. "I have to send twenty copies to Rishon-le-Zion. My friend Chaim will probably agree to distribute the paper, collect the money, and work on subscribers. We can also send a few copies to Jaffa. Lolik can be our agent there."

With the money they received they bought stamps, prepared two large parcels, and posted them.

"There is little profit left," said Baruch.

"It makes no difference. When the money starts

coming in from Rishon and Jaffa we are going to see real profits," said Ben-Zion. "And anyhow, money is not that important. The main thing is that we are doing something really worthwhile. We are spreading the Hebrew language among children. Everybody is going to praise us for our work. You just wait and see. We are going to be really respected for our work."

The boys went their way, and Ben-Zion went home.

On the way home he thought, Abba will be proud of me! This should make him feel less unhappy. And Amma will also be delighted. I am going to give them a copy of the paper with my very own autograph!

He was very excited when he arrived home. But to his surprise he discovered that his father was in a rage.

"Is this your work?" Ben-Yehudah roared, shoving the sheet with the articles about the borders of the country in Ben-Zion's face.

"Yes, we're publishing a children's paper. We call it *The Hebrew Language*. It's written only in Hebrew," Ben-Zion stammered, unable to grasp what had gone wrong this time. "I thought you'd be so pleased—"

"Pleased? Do you know what you've written, child? You are a dreamer! You would like the borders of our country to extend from the River Nile to the Euphrates. You claim that all the Arab territories should be part and parcel of Israel because Jethro was the father-in-law of Moses. Do you want the stolen homeland back or do you want me to go to prison again? I told you a thousand times, Ben-Zion—worry about your own affairs! Politics is not for children!

You will only cause me a great deal of trouble with all your cute tricks!"

Ben-Yehudah was furious and frightened. His enemies had another opening. People had begun to gossip. Word spread that Ben-Yehudah had found a way to get around the banning of *Hatzvi*. Now he was publishing under the guise of putting out a children's paper.

The next day five armed Turkish soldiers entered the house and started a search.

"Where is the paper? Where did you publish this material?" they asked sternly, turning the house upside down.

Ben-Zion slipped out the back entrance, carrying the copying machine and the papers under his coat, together with the paper, the ink, and anything else which could endanger them with the Turks. He threw everything into the Mamillah Pond with a broken heart. He watched the machine disappear and stared at the paper and the other treasures slowly sinking to the bottom of the pond. A ripple grew slowly and spread on the water, until it was also lost. Ben-Zion's newspaper had come to an end.

## * twenty-six

Since Ben-Yehudah was not allowed to publish his paper, he spent all his time working on the dictionary. He worked eighteen and sometimes nineteen hours a day. He was indifferent to his surroundings; his mind was only on his work. He was not concerned with the family, nor did he try to find out where and how Chemdah was obtaining food for them all. He did not notice that his children ate black bread and oil for breakfast and supper, and that often they had no lunch because there was no food at home. Chemdah did her best to try to find some food for her family. But ever since the paper had closed down, there had been no money in the house. Eliezer never gave it a thought. He did not notice Chemdah's attempts to borrow money to pay back loans and to collect old debts from past subscribers to the paper.

Eliezer Ben-Yehudah had never been a devoted father. Still, during that period he seemed to grow even further away from them. He had no patience with them and tried to make sure that they did not get in his way when he was working.

"Hush, children! Your father is working," Chemdah would greet them when they returned from school. They were not allowed to talk loudly, to sing, or to laugh when they were home. They used to walk on tiptoe in order not to disturb their father. They were not permitted to bring friends home or to play in the garden or near the house.

"Go out and play in the street," Chemdah would whisper to them. "I will soon be done with my work, and then we'll take a nice walk." The atmosphere in the house was close and oppressive. The grim shadow of a busy and irritable father seemed to hang about in the air all the time.

Sometimes when they were playing in the street,

Chemdah would call out, "Come inside, children. Your father wants you!" They knew what this meant. They would enter their father's study quietly, while he went through his pockets. He would take out a small piece of paper and hand it over to them. Another one of Ben-Yehudah's new words had to be taken out into the street. In those days, that was the only time he addressed them.

"Here you are," he would say. "I have made up a new Hebrew word for 'concert.' From now on it will be called *tizmoret*. Next week a violinist from Rehovoth is going to play at the Alliance school. The playing must be referred to as a *tizmoret*. People must become familiar with this word. I want as many people as possible to hear the word *tizmoret* by next week. Now, go outside and see how people react to the word."

*"Tizmoret,"* repeated Ben-Zion. "Fine. I'll remember this word." He knew that he had to be very careful with the pronounciation; on no account should he distort it.

"Go on, out with you!" Ben-Yehudah's temper was beginning to wear thin.

"All we are to him is messengers of his words. His words are dearer to him than his children," muttered Ben-Zion.

"I enjoy it," said Penina. "It's nice to be the first person who uses a new word in a language. I would like to think that if the word took root and people began using it, I was the first one to hear it and that I helped to make it known."

"Oh yes, it's all right when people accept a new word," said Yoseph. "But sometimes people think his words are terribly funny, and then they laugh at him and us. Remember the time he tried to introduce the word 'prithee' instead of 'please' "?

"Come on, kids, let's go," said Yemima. "There's a man standing over there on the corner. We can go over to him and ask him when the *tiz*—the whatsitsname, Ben-Zion?—takes place."

*"Tizmoret. Tiz-mo-ret!* Come on, let's go over to him. I hope he's in a good mood."

One evening the younger children had had their supper and had gone to bed. But Ben-Zion was still out. Eliezer stood by his desk, lost in his work, not noticing his son's absence. Chemdah paced worriedly and impatiently about the room. At midnight she could hear the sound of approaching footsteps. She rushed to the door and saw Ben-Zion tiptoeing into his room.

"Where have you been, you bad boy?" she asked crossly. "I was terribly worried about you. What happened to you?"

"After school I went over to David's. We did our homework together. Then his parents invited me to stay for supper. I couldn't refuse, so I stayed. After supper we began talking and I didn't realize how late it was. David's father told us about his childhood in a small town in Russia. We told him about our school. We spent the whole evening talking to him, and he was not too busy for us and he was never angry. He treated us as if we were his friends. It was so pleasant there. Why isn't my father more like David's?"

"Your father is simply not like other fathers. Your father is a great man. He is the reviver of the

Hebrew language. You should be proud of him and his life's work."

"Oh yes, I know all that. But why must he be a great man? Sometimes I'm jealous of kids who have an ordinary father, not a great man for a father. Kids who have a real home."

"Isn't ours a real home?" asked Chemdah, and Ben-Zion could detect the note of pain in her voice.

"It's different here. You can't even talk in here! I always feel so cramped at home. I never feel at ease. There are so many things I can't do at home. I can't have my friends over! Do you call this a home, Amma?"

"This is our home, child, and you must learn to accept it the way it is. I do my best to try and make it as pleasant as possible for you. Just see how nicely I've fixed up your room. It's even got pictures on the walls. I'm sorry you don't like it here."

"Oh, Amma, you're so good. You're really good." Ben-Zion looked up at the woman standing beside him. She was young enough to be his elder sister. "I love you, Amma. I really do. I love you with all my heart. The kids are all jealous of me because I have such a young and pretty mother. I love you." Ben-Zion hugged Chemdah's waist affectionately. Suddenly he let go, looked at her, winked, and said, "Amma, I've just discovered something strange. Your tummy is so big!"

Chemdah blushed. "So, you've discovered my secret, have you? You're a real scamp."

"What would you like it to be this time, a boy or a girl?" he asked mischievously, treating himself as her confidant.

"I want it to be a boy. Then I will be able to name it Ehud, after the baby I lost." Suddenly her eyes were full of pain.

She doesn't have an easy time, either, thought Ben-Zion. She always smiles outwardly, she is always happy, bolstering everybody's spirits, but she keeps everything that hurts her deep down in her heart.

"I wanted to tell you something funny that happened to me in school today," he said, trying to distract her. "This morning—"

"Chemdah!" Eliezer's voice boomed from his study. "I lost a word, Chemdah!"

"What? Again?" said Chemdah, rising to her feet. "Your story will have to wait until tomorrow. Come along and help me look for the word."

They entered Eliezer's study, which, as usual, was terribly untidy. There were notes in Eliezer's poor handwriting all over the desk, floor, and chairs. Books were piled high on the floor. Look for a single word in this chaos! They shook out books. Every scrap of paper was carefully turned over and examined.

Finally Chemdah grew desperate. "Eliezer, perhaps you should go through your pockets, maybe . . ."

Sure enough, in one of his pockets he discovered a tiny, wrinkled piece of paper, and the word which had somehow eluded his memory was scribbled on it. Chemdah gave a deep sigh of relief. "I'm glad we found it," she said. But Eliezer had no time to thank them or even to apologize. He immediately went back to his papers and noted the word down in his thick notebook.

"Good night, Ben-Zion," whispered Chemdah to

the boy. "It's very late. You won't be able to get up in the morning."

## * *twenty-seven*

Summer was Ben-Zion's favorite time of the year. But this was the most wonderful summer he had ever known. As in previous summers there was no school, and he could roam outside the city. He climbed over rocky mountains, inhaling the fresh and clear Jerusalem air. He was intoxicated by the open spaces. This was the summer that he first experienced a new and wonderful emotion. A young girl had moved into the house across the street. Her name was Leah.

Ben-Zion fell in love with Leah. It was his first love, and his heart felt as if it would burst. Dainty, dark-haired, black-eyed Leah evoked wonderful feelings in Ben-Zion. He used to sit by the window and watch the garden where she sat each evening, and his heart would overflow with love.

She is so pretty. Life is so wonderful. I feel fine. I feel great, Ben-Zion would say to himself.

Life seemed to be improving for the Ben-Yehudah family. Chemdah gave birth to a son, whom she named Ehud. She was happy and she sang all day long. She lavished all her love on the baby. It was a double love: a love for the babe in her arms and for the one she had lost.

And one day Baron Rothschild's representative arrived with wonderful news. The baron had approached the authorities, who had agreed to cancel the ban against the paper and allow Ben-Yehudah to publish it again. The family was overjoyed.

"But a year isn't over yet since they banned the publication of the paper," wondered Ben-Zion.

"The baron can work miracles, child," said Chemdah, looking at Eliezer happily. He seemed to have revived and returned to the land of the living. All the articles which had been like a hidden flame within him were written that very evening.

"There is so much I have to say in my paper. There are hundreds of new words which I have added to the language in this brief period. I will have to add a page or two," he told Chemdah with shining eyes.

That weekend, when *Hatzvi* was again on sale, the residents of Jerusalem bought it and read it fervently. There were many new subscribers in Jerusalem, Jaffa, and the settlements. Money flowed into the house once more. The family began to eat three meals a day again, and the Ben-Yehudah home overflowed with visitors, as in the past. Now that the authorities looked upon him favorably and the baron backed him openly, Ben-Yehudah's worst enemies were careful not to voice their resentment aloud.

That was the summer when Ben-Yehudah completed his dictionary. He was overcome with excitement when he held the first printed copy of the dictionary in his hands.

"Here is the first copy of our Hebrew dictionary," he said to Chemdah, handing her a thin book bound in gray cardboard. He was very proud of the book. It did not matter to him that it contained only forty

אליעזר בן־יהודה
מחיה הלשון העברית
**ELIEZER BEN-YEHUDA**
RENOVATEUR DE LA
LANGUE HÉBRAÏQUE

pages, and that it was printed on third-grade yellow paper and looked shabby and poor. "This is only the beginning. The day will come, Chemdah, when I will put out a large, complete dictionary. It will contain many volumes."

But it seemed to be ordained that happiness would not stay long in the Ben-Yehudah home. Dvorah became sick, the happy little girl who was nicknamed the jolly prophetess because she was always happy, singing and dancing. She would always look lovely with her flowing long hair and her straight, lithe body.

"It is a slight cold," said the doctor. But the cold turned into a serious illness. Dvorah lay in her bed for many weeks, feverish and unable to breathe properly.

"Please, doctor. Make sure that nothing happens to the child. Nothing must happen to her. Please help her," begged her mother, with tears streaming down her face.

The doctor's efforts were useless. The expensive medicines, the devoted nursing, did not help. Dvorah's face grew more and more pale from day to day, her body became thinner, and her eyes lost their brightness. One Saturday morning, in the middle of winter, the girl whispered to her mother who was sitting beside her, "Imma, I know I am never going to see the stars again."

"Don't say such a thing, darling." Chemdah was very upset as she stroked the burning forehead. "You will soon be healthy again, and you will be able to go out and play. We shall go for lovely walks to the hillside, and we shall pick many beautiful flowers." Dvorah did not reply.

The house was still. Eliezer had gone out to visit

his friend, Nissim. The children had left for a walk. Chemdah and her sick child were alone in the house. Suddenly the girl sat upright, terrified. "What's wrong?" she whimpered. "I can't see you, Imma. I can't see a thing. It's so dark!" Her head fell back on the pillow and her body twitched for a moment. Then she stopped moving.

Chemdah slid down on her knees before the bed. "Why, why again?" she cried.

Ben-Zion burst into the house, happy and excited. He was holding a large bouquet of red cyclamens. He had just come back from a walk with Leah and her brother. He had given Leah a large bunch of wild flowers which he had picked in the field, and she had handed him the bouquet of cyclamens, which she had picked with her own fair hands.

"Look at these gorgeous cyclamens, Amma. I feel so happy! Amma? Amma, where are you?"

"Why, why again?" He heard the sound of crying. He ran to Dvorah's room and saw his sister on the bed. He realized immediately what had happened, for he had seen death before. He spread the red flowers around Dvorah's small head without a word.

"She loved flowers so," he whispered as he knelt next to Chemdah, hugging her.

When the husky men from the burial society arrived, they were very shocked. They found a small girl, surrounded by red cyclamens.

"Flowers on a dead body?" asked one of them angrily.

"Is Ben-Yehudah such an infidel that he doesn't know that this is not done?" exclaimed another.

"Sacrilege!" said a third, spitting in disgust.

"The flowers have defiled the child's body. She will not be buried according to Jewish rites."

"Shut your filthy mouths!" screamed Eliezer hoarsely. "Get out of here. Tell everybody that I will bury my child in my own garden. I shall dig the grave with my own hands. I do not need your services. Let everybody in Jerusalem know what I think of you and your rites!" He left the room, stumbling, and went to the garden, where he picked up a spade and began to dig.

The news spread through Jerusalem like wildfire. Everybody was excited. Even Ben-Yehudah's sworn enemies thought the matter had been carried too far.

That afternoon the grave diggers returned to the house, their heads bent low. The family set out on its journey along the familiar path.

When the grave was covered, Ben-Zion's world seemed to grow very dark. His mother's large grave loomed out of the darkness; alongside it were the five small graves. He burst into tears.

## * *twenty-eight*

The loss had a strange effect on Ben-Zion. Overnight he seemed to have grown mature. He became serious and no longer ran around boisterously in the streets of Jerusalem. He spoke quietly and with reserve and conducted himself like a person who had taken on heavy responsibilities. Chemdah, who became sick from shock and grief, shifted some of her work to him. He made certain that the children prepared their homework and saw to it that they were quiet when their father was working. He bought oil and flour from the vendors who passed by their house. In the evening he would put his good suit on and go out with his father to help him collect money from subscribers and to mail newspapers to subscribers in Jaffa and the villages.

With his dark suit, light hair, and gray-blue eyes, he was a very handsome lad. He was tall and slim, and when he walked in the street, girls would peek at him through their windows. But Ben-Zion ignored them. All his thoughts were of Leah.

He loved her deeply and she was on his mind constantly, yet he did not have the courage to tell her. He would sit at his windowsill, waiting for her to come out to the garden. Whenever he saw her, he jumped back into the room so that she would not see him. At night he wrote poems full of ardent love, but he never dared to show them to her.

One evening when he stood at the window, he saw Leah sitting in the garden eating a tomato. She seemed very lovely in her blue dress with her white teeth biting the red, ripe tomato. She seems like a picture, he thought. I must go and speak to her. He stood up. His heart beat wildly as he opened the gate to the courtyard.

"Hello, Ben-Zion," she smiled. "Would you like a tomato?" she said, handing him a ripe vegetable from her basket.

"No thanks. I don't want a tomato, I want . . ." he began stammering and then fell silent. He wanted to tell her that he loved her.

His courage failed him at the very last moment.

"What were you going to say, Ben-Zion?" she asked.

"I wanted to tell you . . . I want us to be friends."

"Aren't we friends?" she asked.

"Yes, but I mean . . . a different kind of friendship. You know what I mean. You and me. That's what I mean. I would like you to become my girl friend. . . . I want to be your regular boy friend. . . . Do you agree?"

He waited tensely for her answer.

"Yes, Ben-Zion. We'll be friends, as you said," she replied with lowered eyes.

"I watch you every day through the window," he told her.

"I know. . . . that's why I always go out," she said.

"You mean to say that you've known about it all the time?" he asked, somewhat embarrassed to have been found out.

"Yes."

"Well, why didn't you say anything? We could have been friends ages ago!"

"The boy must be the first to speak," she said with a smile.

"There is something I must tell you. I have written many poems for you."

"Really? Poems for me? That sounds wonderful," she whispered.

"You are so pretty."

The evening had suddenly changed. The wind

was tender, the sunset lovelier. They felt good. They had only exchanged a few sentences, and suddenly everything had become so simple and easy.

Now came wonderful days and evenings, the time of love.

When Ben-Zion awakened in the morning his first thought would be, Leah! No, it's not a dream. She really is my girl. She loves me. I am soon going to get up and see her.

They went for long walks on the hills of Jerusalem, hand in hand. At night, they sat close to each other, their very silence marking their love.

When they walked in the street, everybody turned to look at them. Ben-Zion, who was tall and slim, and Leah, a slight, petite, dark-eyed, black-haired beauty, who wore a shy smile on her lovely face.

Love was great! Life was good! Ben-Zion's heart was full of warmth and tenderness. He loved everything under the sun.

The world does indeed seem wonderful to young people in love.

## * *twenty-nine*

One evening Eliezer called Ben-Zion to his study and told him, "Son, I have decided to send you to Paris to study. You are to leave next month."

"To Paris?" Ben-Zion was shocked. "Why can't I study here?"

"I am dissatisfied with the standards of the schools in Jerusalem. You will study in Paris."

"But I don't want to go. I am not going!" Ben-Zion cried angrily.

His father had made his decision. It was impossible to argue with him. Ben-Zion went out slowly and shut himself in his room. He sat at the window facing Leah's garden. Go to Paris? Leave Leah, his only love? No! He couldn't possibly do it. But what was he going to do? Could he explain his feelings to his father? Was it possible to discuss love with him? What does he know of love?

There was a knock on the door.

"Who is it?" he called out.

"It's me, Chemdah," replied the soft voice. "Open the door, dear, I want to talk to you."

"Leave me alone," he whispered, standing up and facing the door. "I know you. You will only find an excuse for him. You always join with him against me."

He was furious. He lay on the bed, looked up at the ceiling. And then he started to weep. He lay there until he heard Chemdah moving away from his door.

Night fell. Darkness settled upon Ben-Zion through the windows. He felt surrounded by the dark. It was choking him.

"Open the door, Ben-Zion," his father's voice called out to him. "There is something I would like to make clear to you."

Ben-Zion stood up. He dried the tears with his sleeve and opened the door. His father stood on the threshold. Suddenly Ben-Zion noticed that he was taller than his father. For the first time in his life he realized just how small and frail his father was.

Eliezer entered the room and sat on the bed. "Sit down," he told his son. "Let's talk."

They sat in silence for a few minutes, and Ben-Zion thought, What can he add to all the arguments I've heard before? I've heard his speeches a thousand times already. I know everything he has to say.

"Do you know, son, that you are very dear to me?" asked Eliezer quietly.

For a moment, Ben-Zion was taken aback. These words were so unexpected, so unlike his father. But soon he pulled himself together. "Is it your son who is dear to you, or is it the first Hebrew child?" he asked his father sarcastically.

"It is you, my eldest son, you who are also the first Hebrew child. I cannot separate the two. Just as I cannot separate myself from the Hebrew language," Eliezer told him as he took his son's hand in his own. "You are the dearest person in the world to me. I have never shown you much affection, nor have I ever spoiled you. I simply had no time for such things. But I hope that, in spite of everything, you do know of my true feelings for you. I believe that when you are a man, the day will come when you too will fight for your way of life and for your ideals. You will have children of your own, and you will want to raise them as you see fit. Only then, son, will you be able to understand me and no longer be angry with me."

"Yes, Abba, I understand. But I find it so difficult at times. . . ." whispered Ben-Zion.

"True. It is difficult. Our battle for the revival of

the Hebrew language was very difficult, and as in every other war there were casualties along the way. You, my son, who stood in the first line of fire, were one of those casualties. But believe me, Ben-Zion, I had no alternative. It was essential that I prove to the world that a child could be raised in the Hebrew language. And you proved it. Hebrew has not yet won its final victory, but it is getting closer to that victory every day.

"And I believe, son, that the day is not far off when Hebrew will be the spoken language in this country. Babies will utter their first words in Hebrew, schools will teach in Hebrew, university lectures will be given in Hebrew. Books, plays, and poetry will be written in Hebrew. Doctors will treat their patients in Hebrew. Captains will sail ships in Hebrew. Hebrew will be heard everywhere; it will be our language. When that day comes, my son, you will know that it was because of you and all the people who fought and suffered in this cause."

Ben-Zion could remember another conversation with his mother, Dvorah, who had told him the same things many years ago. But at that time he had been a small boy and could not grasp the meaning of her words. Now he understood. He could already see the first results of his father's efforts. Yet his mother had not lived to see it. She had been one of the first casualties. She would never know that her tears and sorrow and suffering had not been in vain.

"Abba, do you think that, in days to come, the people who will speak Hebrew will remember us?" he asked, as his eyes filled with tears. Suddenly he was appalled at the thought that when the day came, and everyone spoke Hebrew, people might not remember his mother, the first Hebrew mother. He could remember a verse from the Book of Jeremiah: "I remember for thee the affection of thy youth, The love of thine espousals; How thou wentest after Me in the wilderness, In a land that was not sown." Then he recalled that his father had quoted that verse in his eulogy of his mother.

"Yes, son," said Eliezer, seeming to read his innermost thoughts. "When that day comes, everybody is going to remember your mother, and you, and me —and every one of us."

"Imma told me once that one day I would be proud of having been a guinea pig. But it was very difficult. There were times when I actually hated you for your strictness and for the things you made me do. But today I can see that if you had been less stubborn and had given in to me, you wouldn't have been able to win your battle."

"I am pleased that you understand, son," said Eliezer, his face showing his relief and happiness.

"But there is one thing that I cannot understand," said Ben-Zion. "Why are you sending me away?"

"Ben-Zion," said Eliezer, his face assuming that look of stubbornness and deep conviction, "you are not just a boy. You are the first Hebrew child. For many people you symbolize something. If you grow up and become an educated man with wide horizons and intelligence, I will have succeeded in proving that it is possible to bring up a generation of cultured young people in the Hebrew language. If you fail, however, it will not be you who fails, nor will it be my failure. The revival of the Hebrew language will fail.

Believe me, son, I will find it very difficult to part from you. Especially after this evening, when I have discovered you are not merely my son but my comrade too. The expense will also be considerable, and I still have no idea how I am going to raise the funds for your studies. But you must do it. You must go out to the world for an education. The first Hebrew child must be given the very best there is!"

"Being the first Hebrew child is so difficult," whispered Ben-Zion.

"Son," said Eliezer, "once you told me that you wanted to be an editor, like me."

"Yes," replied Ben-Zion. "I would like to be an *itonai.*"

"*Itonai?* Why, Ben-Zion, this is a fine word you have just invented. A man working on an *iton* is an *itonai.* I must write it down immediately, and I am going to put it into my dictionary. Go, son, go and study. Then we shall be able to work together—Ben-Yehudah the father and Ben-Yehudah the son."

"No, Abba," Ben-Zion said. "I am going to change my name when I become a journalist. I have already picked a name out. I will change my name to Itamar —which is the name Imma and you first meant to call me when I was born. My last name will be Ben-Avi, made up of the initials of your name,* Ben Eliezer Ben-Yehudah. What do you think of it?"

"I like the name Itamar Ben-Avi very much indeed," said the father, hugging his son's shoulder.

That very week they began making preparations.

*In Hebrew, the initials of Eliezer Ben-Yehudah—aleph, bet, yod—can be pronounced Avi.

Cases were packed, passports stamped, words of departure and farewell were heard.

"Don't forget me, my Leah," Ben-Zion whispered. "Write to me often. I will write to you every day. Remember that I love you very much."

"I will never forget you, Ben-Zion."

On a summer morning in the month of Av, Ben-Zion stood on the deck of a boat which was moving slowly off the port of Jaffa. He gazed at the shore. He could see his father lift his hand in farewell. He remembered the words his father had whispered in his ear. "You are the dearest person in the world to me." The words caressed his heart.

His father's image grew hazy and disappeared. The beach was far away. Now Ben-Zion stood between the heaven and the sea. To the east lay the land of Israel. His childhood. His memories—both pleasant and sad. The six graves in Jerusalem, and Leah, his love, and his father's home. To the west—the great ocean; behind it the unknown, a new world, a new era, maturity.

I am Itamar Ben-Avi, he said to himself with a smile. I am a journalist from the land of Israel. He stuck his hands in his pockets and walked toward the prow of the boat.